W9-BGF-693

The Broken Snare

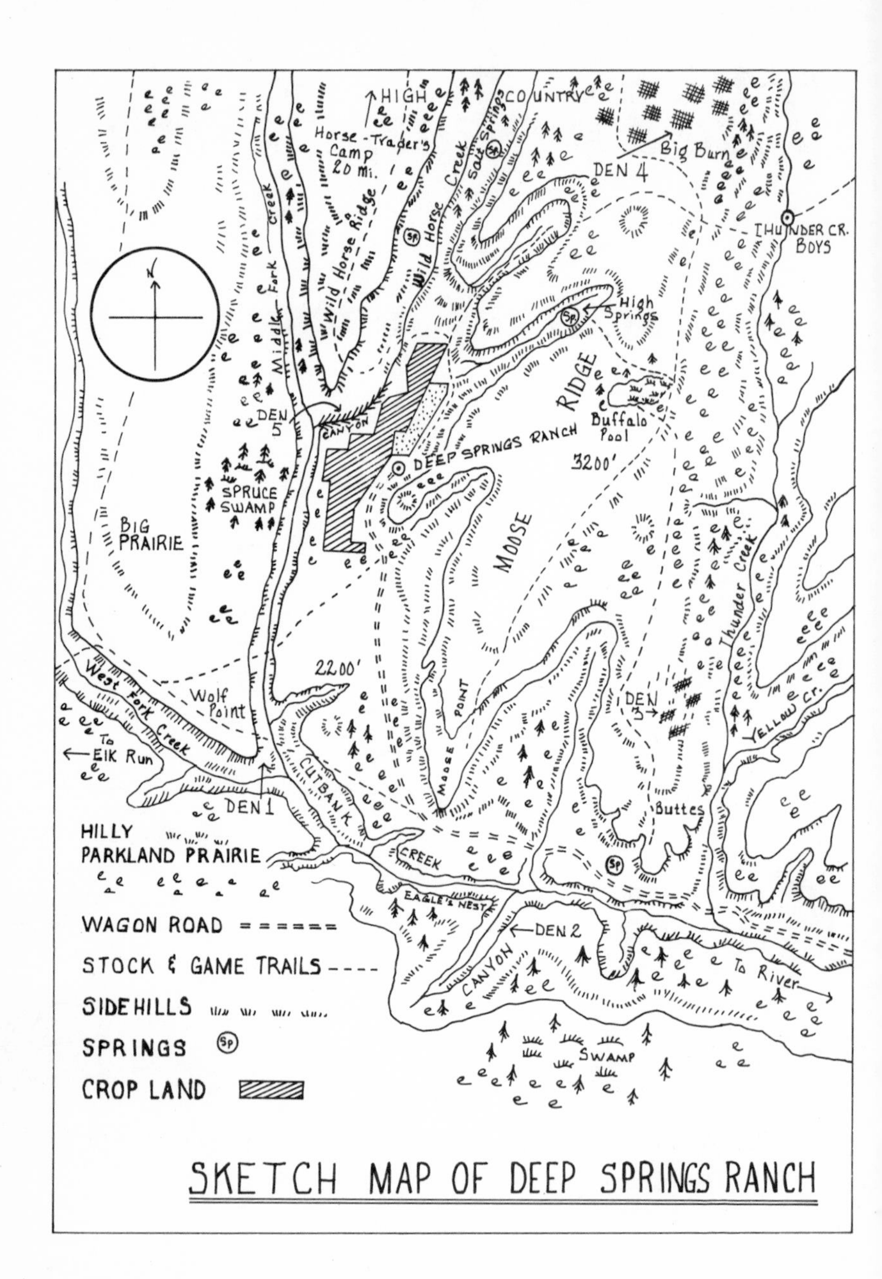

SKETCH MAP OF DEEP SPRINGS RANCH

The Broken Snare

R. D. SYMONS

All Flesh Is Grass. St. Peter

1970

Doubleday & Company, Inc., Garden City, New York
Doubleday Canada Limited, Toronto, Ontario

LIBRARY OF CONGRESS CATALOG CARD NUMBER 70–97711

PRINTED IN THE UNITED STATES OF AMERICA
9 8 7 6 5 4 3 2

Introduction

What do you do when you are trapped?

Once a man and his family asked themselves that question.

He was a rancher by choice. But the Great Depression finished what invading homesteaders had started, and he went broke.

A government job saved the day, financially. But new outlooks, new methods, and the machine age threatened to make him no longer a dedicated man, but a hack; a mere cog in a machine.

So he escaped with little capital, but a high heart, to a new frontier. A rugged country of foothills, with none of the amenities of "civilization." How he did so; how he, reluctantly, upset an ecological balance, is told here.

The reactions of wolf, bear, and moose to each other and to man is parallelled by pioneer man's reaction to them and to modern man.

How he, in turn, found himself trapped once more by the very forces he had withdrawn from forms the ending of this story.

Prologue

The Man, mounted and leading a pack-horse, had come to the valley from the east. He was looking for grass, water, and building timber. Now, from a high ridge he looked down on a mile-wide valley, with a creek looping and winding on the far side—a creek he could not see, but which he knew was there, because he saw the shadowed cleft and the tops of trees which jutted above the valley floor.

Below, and a little to the north, a clump of spruce trees made a dark, spired blotch. He touched his horse and angled down the steep, grassy slope, the led-horse eager, following on a slack rope.

It was over a mile from the top of the ridge to the spruce, a mile in which the Man's eye took in all the details—the blue-stem wheat grass, the clumps of saskatoon bushes, the wild sages, the tangles of rose-briars and snowberry. To the right and left, winding, wooded coulees showed the smoky grey of unleafed poplar, with occasional dark spruces in contrast.

This valley looked the very mate to the Battle Creek valley of the Cypress Hills in the border cattle country he had known as a young man. It was hard to believe that five hundred miles north and as many miles west that favoured spot could be repeated.

The mountains, now, were something different, and as he looked at the frieze of their blue and jagged peaks, the Man knew that the moisture-laden chinook must surely blow across them. The Pacific was not so far away, he thought.

In the shadow of the spruce the Man found what he half expected—two springs of clear, cold water.

He camped, made his fire, hobbled his horses, and slept. His last waking thought was that he would have to rise early. He knew there was a base-line five miles to the south; his map showed this—but the survey was dated twenty years back.

He had to stake his land, and to do this he would have to work from a point on the base-line—the township corner mound and pits. But years of fallen trees, bush fires, and new growth of saplings and grass would make that hard to locate. He would leave the pack-horse tethered at what he now called Deep Springs, and be in the saddle by daybreak.

The sun was in the west, but the Black Wolf started his hunting early, travelling south and east towards Moose Ridge. Just before reaching it he turned south, and after a moment's indecision turned east again, following a faint game-trail which meandered through the tall grass and young trees with which the base-line was overgrown. On either side were taller, older trees. Criss-crossed among the young growth lay many dry and half-rotted giants which the wind had laid about at all angles, some with their tops still held by greener trees across the line.

Only a practised woodsman would know that once this had been a cleared line, straight as a knife-cut through the bush; for even the stumps from the cutting were now rotted and mossy, some pushed over by moose; and only that same practised eye would be able to discern that they had been cut by an axe.

Coming to a grass-grown mound, surrounded by pits which might have been made by the falling of a tree uprooted in the soft soil, the Black Wolf paused. Here were fresh horse tracks, the warm horse-smell. The wolf was used to horses in bands, but a single horse was a rare thing. Perhaps it was a mare with a foal. That would be luck. It was hard to separate a mare from her bunch . . . and foals were his favourite prey.

The track went north, and he followed.

What could this horse be doing? Perfectly straight it had gone, stepping over fallen logs it could have swung around, through willow brush it could have avoided, across swampy pools in which most horses would not have muddied their fetlocks.

The trail left the woods, leading straight up the steepest slope of Moose Point and on to the ridge; ignoring the easier grade of the wild-horse trail which looped and zig-zagged more gradually upward.

The Black Wolf could now see the wide valley of Cutbank Creek to the west; and to the east the narrower cleft of Burnt Creek, a tangled boscage of willow swamps and fallen, blackened spruce snags; beyond that again, the buttes of Thunder Creek.

For over four miles the Black Wolf had followed the horse-smell. The afternoon was still, and the scent was not as high as his nose but down there in the hoof-prints towards which he from time to time lowered his muzzle. All at once the Black Wolf stood rooted. He heard a voice just ahead, beyond a clump of spruce and poplar.

"Well, old Fox, here's where I want the corner of my land. I'll get to work; and you, old-timer—well done, and graze a bit."

The tall sorrel lowered his blazed face and began to tear the bush-grass, while the Black Wolf watched the two from a patch of alders.

The Man dismounted, drew a government form from his chaps' pocket, wrote briefly, and tacked the white sheet to a tree, which he first blazed with a hand axe.

He stood back to admire and read:

> *I intend to apply for permission to purchase the following lands, situate approximately 5 miles north of the corner of Township "C" in the Land Recording District of "D," commencing at this point, thence 80 chains west, thence 80 chains north, thence 80 chains east, thence 80 chains south to the point of commencement, and containing 640 acres more or less. The purpose of this purchase is stock raising. Signed. . . .*

"Good," said the Man aloud. "That's a section. Tomorrow I'll stake two more in the valley for the other two. Pity the Kid isn't eighteen yet. That'll be three sections—about two thousand acres. At two bucks an acre—gosh! The down payment'll be two hundred! Then later we'll stake three sections for grazing lease among these open hills, and we'll have the cream of the country—and lots of room for expansion later. Fox!" turning to the sorrel, "bless you for a steady walker—a chain-crew couldn't have done better."

He closed the notebook into which he had jotted his tallies of the horse's measured strides, and snapping shut his old army compass, pocketed both. He mounted and started down to his camp. It was dusk now.

Fox shied suddenly and snorted.

The Man said: "Don't fool around. I'm hungry."

Neither saw the dark shape loping westward down a brushy gully.

They reached camp. The waiting pack-mare whinnied with relief at the thump of hooves. Fox stopped by the cold ashes and looked mildly around at his rider's spurred foot. It was time to unsaddle. The Man turned Fox loose with a smack on the rump—Fox would never leave the mare.

As he cooked his supper, the Man was already making plans to bring the Woman, the Boy, and the Kid to this spot as soon as he had made his recording in the Land Office. There'd be a lot of work. There was no wild hay. The tall, waving grass of the flatland was so beset with burnt stumps, willow clumps, and fallen timber that to mow it would be impossible. It would have to be cleared. And then? Well, it might as well be ploughed. He'd seed it to brome grass, which would yield more hay per acre and keep the wild brush from re-establishing itself. It would take time, but it was the kind of challenge he was looking for . . .

The kind he knew he could tackle.

The Broken Snare

Chapter 1

The Black Wolf raised his head, then slipped quietly from his sunny lookout on the high, eroded point above the gravel bar where the West Fork joined Cutbank Creek. In the shelter of some low brush he halted, muzzle still to the south.

Long he looked; and each time he heard that faint jingling, that dull click of a hoof on deadfall, his hackles rose and his eyes narrowed to pin-points.

He knew horses. He knew the wild troops which trotted each evening from the windswept uplands to cool their throats in the deep-gullied creek below. He knew them as the Beaver Indians knew moose—for they were part of his living. Nearly half the annual drop of foals fell to him and his kind.

These thudding sounds meant horses. But they must mean something else too. The free bands of the high country rarely followed the winding game-trails of the valley floor without scattering out to crop the grass. And mares with foals made no such clinking sounds as now came to his ears.

The Black Wolf padded silently down the crooked game-path, crossed the creek to the south-east, and warily worked his upward way to the top of a cutbank.

The wind was not strong, and the soft breath it sent through the crested poplars merely eddied and sank to earth on their north-west side.

The wolf stood like a statue, his form and outline lost in the shadow cast by a patch of saskatoon shrubs. His nostrils quivered when he saw the horses emerge from the rolling, scrubby lowlands and start to string out across a brief prairie. Something was wrong. Not their single-file, plodding progress; that was the processional arrangement he knew so well—an old matriarch mare in the lead, younger mares and their gambolling foals next, then the yearlings and two-year-olds, and finally a stallion guarding the rear. That was accepted.

But these horses were hump-backed and they jingled. And there was another sound. A sound he had heard once before.

Then, too, there had been horses, and the wolf and his three-footed mate had circled the camp when a sickle moon had dropped behind the distant ridge beyond Big Prairie.

One mare had had a foal, and the wolves' jowls had shaken at the prospect of a juicy feast. But the mare had moved away with a thump of her hobbled feet and a clink of metal, and they had snuffed first the acrid odour of the hobble-links—a fearful smell and a terrifying one—and then the man-scent, which had come in sickening waves from the huddled figures inside the little tent.

His memory fully aroused, the Black Wolf now strained every sense to understand what went on three hundred yards from the creek bank.

Then a human voice said, "Not much further now. The springs are right over there, by that clump of spruce." It was the voice he had heard on Moose Ridge.

The Black Wolf's instinct was to flee—to turn tail, to streak away—keeping the low bushes between himself and the cavalcade until he reached the shelter of the low ground. But he had to be sure, and he turned to snuff the sudden little breeze which bent the grasses and the soft sage, that set the poplar leaves a-dancing.

One snuff was enough.

The Black Wolf fled.

The Cow Moose was restless, and it puzzled her lanky yearling. He had been born the year before in the heavy willows at the foot of the Tumbling Hills, those rounded knolls which here joined the valley to the foot of the steep escarpment of Moose

Ridge. He had been puzzled then, too, when the frosts and snows of early winter had dried up his mother's fountain; when she had moved away or butted him from her flank. But his milk teeth were being replaced, and he had found another use for his rapidly growing rubbery lip: He had now learnt to strip the twigs of alders, willows, and poplars side by side with the cow.

Now the Cow Moose was avoiding him more and more and butted at him more pettishly if he crowded against her.

She was thin after the hard winter, her long hair matted, shaggy and fading rapidly under the late April sun. Thin but heavy with a burden already ripening.

Day by day the two moose worked downhill from the crest of the ridge, always feeding a little lower on the slope, as the buds began to swell on the saskatoon bushes and the geese to call from overhead.

Then, one evening, they stood on the last of the rolling knolls. The Cow Moose looked long into the valley and turned her solemn face to the south, where the purpled willows formed a brushwood frieze about the tall spruce at Clear Springs. It was nearly dusk, but in the fading twilight a movement had caught her eye.

Something white, something peaked, was there, and now she plainly saw the Man, carrying split wood to the tent. As the moose watched there was the flare of a match, but before the tinder caught, before the soft plume of smoke rose, she had faced the air-current and knew.

Still, this camp was a mile away . . .

The Cow Moose walked purposefully down the hill towards the familiar clump of heavy, impenetrable willows she knew so well; a clump apart, a clump where no Indian had ever camped, where there was no water, and from where there was a clear field of vision on three sides and the shelter of the Tumbling Hills behind. The yearling followed in his awkward and rolling gait, alternately snatching at the low bushes and trotting to catch up.

His mother disappeared in the dense thicket, in which the willows grew in great, many-stemmed clumps, reaching upward for ten or twenty feet before branching out to make a canopy over perhaps five acres. Its underside was so beset by drooping branches and twigs both dry and green that no man could move beneath, unless he reverted to all-fours.

The Cow Moose was seized with sudden pain and lay down; but only briefly, for soon she would have to stand again. She moaned softly after each spasm and looked around for the new life she knew had to come, and soon. The yearling, hearing this, stamped his foot, his young mane bristling and his eyes puzzled, backing away from this strange behaviour. Then, full-fed, he, too, lay down, his head to his flank, his velvety nostrils directed to the desultory movements of the night air.

Daylight began to touch the topmost twigs, but it was still like black velvet under the willows when the Cow Moose turned for the last time and began to lick—each in turn—her two chestnut-coloured calves. So like foals were they (for their lips had not yet swelled) that a stranger to the woods, on seeing them, might have been forgiven had he taken them for just that.

A whisky-jack lit in the willows in time to see the awkward, leggy twins taking their first warm drink, one on either side; to see the hollow, heaving flanks fill up and become rounded.

It was getting light beneath the willows now. A white-throated sparrow piped in long sweet notes as he dropped to the ground to scratch and bustle among the crisp brown leaves.

The jay croaked as he, too, dropped down, intent on the many-veined residue speaking so eloquently of new life. With a scrap in his bill, the bird winged away to some more distant place where, snug in a matted spruce, hungry mouths waited, passing directly over the yearling in noiseless flight. Nevertheless, the young moose was wide awake in an instant. With a quick heave aft and fore he was on his feet. He turned towards the still gloomy depths and heard the soft mother-sounds, smelt blood, and heard strange shufflings, tiny hoof thuds. He grunted once, a questioning grunt that brought no response.

Leaving his calfhood behind, he turned and started up the slope, never stopping till he reached the crest of the Tumbling Hills, above which rose the bulk of Moose Ridge.

To the south he could see three miles of valley. And here, among the scattered clumps of tender-twigged brush, he began his breakfast. Once a twig snapped in the willows below. Once more the jay moved between the purpling willowtops, all set

with golden catkins, and the dark, stiff, prickly evergreen which held its deep and felted nest. But the yearling paid no heed. The morning breeze carried no danger signal.

The Woman stood beside the tent, looking east and north, her hand shading her eyes.

"Come here!" she called, and the Man came to stand beside her, still munching his breakfast bannock. "What's that on the hill?" the Woman asked.

The Man looked long and hard, "A moose, dear. A yearling. I saw him yesterday near the same place, only he was with a cow—his mother, I guess. They run all winter with their mothers, you know, and quite often the next summer. Not exactly following like a calf, but keeping in touch."

"What's happened to the cow moose, then?" asked the Woman, and the Boy, who had joined them, spoke.

"Well, I bet you that cow has hidden away to calve. We'll likely see her in a few days with her new calf—or maybe two."

The Man agreed to this, and they all resumed their breakfast, while close by the horses thumped about in their hobbles, and the smell of the torn, sappy young grass scented the air.

Chapter 2

The valley lay roughly north and south. The view to the north was restricted to some five miles, beyond which lay the High Country, a watershed which, drained by a number of narrow, gullied creeks, sent its gathered flow to merge into one—the large creek called the Cutbank.

This creek flowed on south for a few miles, then abruptly changed direction to the south-east to discharge its burden into the big river which flowed through the mountains of the west, hastening to join the great MacKenzie, adding not only its brown flood, but also mute tree trunks to be washed up on the barren shores of the Arctic Sea—driftwood from the Peace Pass to be carved into strange designs by the squat and hardy people of those inhospitable parts.

These waters had, over long and buried years, cut their own steeply banked valley through the wider, more ancient one which, composed of alluvial soil, now formed the "river flats," which could be cultivated, and which are so characteristic of the country for the first few hundred miles of the Peace River and its tributaries.

Above this more serene valley the several ridges, foothills really, hunched like basking whales. These ridges lay parallel, dividing creek from creek, while at each confluence the waters swept boldly and narrowly down, leaving an exposed and windswept point, such as that used as a lookout by the Black Wolf. Beneath that bleached and sage-studded buttress his den lay safely hidden.

It was here, a week after the moose had slunk into the willows, that another wild mother—the Black Wolf's mate—brought forth new life of her kind from her heavy grey body. There were four short-muzzled, pink-bellied pups—three like her, grey but with more yellowish flanks, and one black like his father. They brought swift relief to her fevered and swollen dugs.

Lying in the cool darkness of the den, the Black Wolf and his mate were equally content, even though all the added mouths would have to be fed.

Last night he had brought in turn a rabbit and a nesting grouse. Now he lay on his lookout. He could hear the dull thud of an axe two miles to the north-east.

The ridges were the summer grazing grounds of the wild-horse bands, their chief place of refuge being the high country towards the watershed. Here they could best fight off the wolves or more easily evade their other enemy, man. And man, within the limits of their range, had meant the two brothers usually referred to as "the horse traders," whose shack was somewhere to the north among the more timbered and remote hills.

The ridges were narrow at the top, a thousand or more feet above the valleys. They were strewn with deadfall, for twelve years before a fire had swept through the green-spired spruce and the orderly array of lofty poplars, across the grassy muskegs and occasional open hilltop, to roar in the close-packed thickets of willows and alders. Now young growth a few feet high thrust their tops through the massive logs which lay with their crests to the north-east as the roaring south-west chinooks had bid them. Only a few blackened stubs, burnt into grotesque shapes, still pointed to the sky.

Along these ridges the hard-beaten horse-trails wound, with many a spider-web of side-trails leading to the springs at the head of the many coulees, or debouching from the fallen tangle to zig-zag down the slopes of short, sweet grass below.

The bands varied in number from a small one of perhaps eleven led by a one-eyed grey mare, with half a dozen daughters and granddaughters, some following yearlings, and a mouse-coloured stallion, to the large hand whose master, a chunky red stallion, had evaded capture by the horse traders at least a dozen times.

The first grazed chiefly in the vicinity of Burnt Creek. The latter preferred the steep slopes of Wild Horse Creek and the Salt Springs, west across the valley from Moose Ridge. Another band ranged in the more level country south of the buttes which marked the confluence of Thunder Creek, and there were several more; one up that creek, the others to the west of Big Prairie, or up the Middle Fork.

Any of the near bands, if put to flight by shouting, weaving riders, would eventually make for the uplands by way of one of the wooded coulees and would take a swinging pace straight up the ridge in the direction of the High Country.

It was those same coulees—gullied, deep, V-sided, and beset with rocks and fallen trees—which made it almost impossible for even a trained saddle-horse to draw abreast of, or turn, the swift-moving single file of the wild ones; almost impossible to "head" and turn them again to the valley.

Once the burnt country was reached, the worst hazards were the fallen giants, which yet, in their prone submission, thrust up from their rotting boles fierce broken-off limbs hardened by fire and as sharp as bayonets. One slip, one fall, and a rider might be pierced or a steed disembowelled.

No two horses, no two riders, could travel abreast on the narrow trails which snaked their way up and down, in and out, sliding down the cutbanks, plunging across treacherous waters, crawling up to the rim-rock; he who wished to outflank the wild steeds in their flight had to draw a tight cinch, have his blood up, and never look down. He had to fly on wings, indeed, as the patron saint of all horses well knew—bold Pegasus, who had more than once heard the curses of a rider and seen a saddle torn from the back of a horse who would run no more.

Not all these horses were originally wild. Most, indeed, were feral stock which had drifted to the hills when their owners in the eastern settlements had replaced their work-teams with tractors—mares with foals, leggy yearlings, unbranded and broken-down geldings. Such groups would keep to themselves for a while, but as they followed the freedom trail from flower-

speckled sidehill to lush woodland meadow, the wild stallions would snuff the mares on the evening breeze and find them and steal them from their poor harness-galled, emasculated relatives. No one wanted the geldings, unless they were small enough and young enough to carry a pack, and unless they were unbranded or "slick." But the mares, to the horse traders, were another matter. Branded they might be, crippled they often were, but they could still raise colts.

The range was unfenced from the settlements to the mountains, and a stray horse might run with a tame, range-broken band or a wild band as it wished, and if the owner wanted her he could ride—a thing no farmer willingly did—and look for her and claim her.

This would cause no embarrassment to the traders. "Shore, take her; you're welcome!" they'd say. But let them have that mare one year, two years, five years, and there would be a colt to brand each year—*after* it was weaned. Well they knew, the traders, that only a sucking foal could be lawfully claimed by the owner of a mare. As for a "slick"—one horse looked much like another to the Law.

Whispers on the wind there might be, but so long as the breeding stock cost nothing, so long as horses could "rustle out" in winter without hay, so long as the market for pack-ponies was good (as it was now), so long as profits swelled, whispers were not proof and would hurt no man whose forbears had lived by the same craft for three generations from the Rio Grande to the Peace. Work was not in their vocabulary; but the swift ride, the telling hours in the saddle, the sweep of the blizzard or the burning sun, the tight belt for the noonday meal—this was not work, not labouring with the shovel, not cringing under the lash of a foreman's tongue!

The Law was only obliged to look briefly; the brands on the pack-horses to be sold to the survey parties were genuine, entered in the Brand Book; and other horse owners were under obligation to guard their property (the Law said) if they didn't wish the horses they turned loose to disappear.

A mare coaxed into a wild band had, in the first year, but a loose alliance with it, so that if hotly pursued she might drop behind with her foal—perhaps with her yearling filly too; and then the riders would close up, and even the wild stallion himself could not say nay to the hissing rope.

It is on the stallion that the protection of a band depends. Not that he leads, that is the job of the oldest and wisest mare. It is by a band's numbers and good flesh that their stallion is judged, and by far the best and wildest band was that which grazed the open slopes and wooded heights of Moose Ridge. The master of these was the chunky, deep-chested animal known as the red stallion, which had long succeeded in keeping his band together despite the cunning and horsemanship of the traders.

Chapter 3

The Man was cutting logs from the straightest and best poplars he could find. He was reluctant to fell even one of the tall spruce trees whose tangled mass of roots below the underbrush of willow and red dogwood kept secret and damp, safe from pollution or drought, the ice-cold pools of Deep Springs.

The only big grove of spruce fit for house timber was over two miles to the north-west, below the shoulder of Wild Horse Point and across the creek of that name. These would have to wait. They could be cut, perhaps, but not hauled until winter, for much of the ground was soft and the creek ran swiftly. Once the snow was deep and the creek frozen . . .

The spot chosen by the Woman for the big house they would build with these logs was a grassy prairie, near but not too near the springs, and below them. It would be sheltered from the north by the tall spruce, protected to the east by the steep slopes of Moose Ridge, which continued four miles south, and open to the south and west, giving a wide view of the mountains on the horizon.

A rough cabin would have to do for now. And it would be best to build farther up the slope, so as not to impede the view later. The young fellows could stop there, but the Woman said she preferred the tent and her bed of spruce boughs, and she had to have some privacy now. Already her face wore that serene look, already she walked in that careful way, already that far-away gaze would have told him, even if she had not spoken, that the boys would soon have (he hoped) a sister.

The Man struck his axe into a stump. The Boy, trimming the limbs of a felled tree, did likewise. Together they sat on the cool trunk and produced the makings.

The Boy pointed up the hill. "Look there," he said. The Man followed the gesture and saw, in a saddle of the hill between two knolls, a movement, a darkening as if a cloud shadow had drifted there. Then they both heard a high-pitched scream, half-anger, half-desire, and they knew that a wild stallion and his troop fed on the hills.

Only in early spring and during the winter did the horses feed to any extent in the open. In spring, when the annual renewal greened the smooth slopes, their wild hooves gashed the early, white-blossomed onions and the silvery lacing of sage. In winter, when the warm chinook swept bare those far prairies, the short, cured grass nourished the bands against the bitter cold and fierce storms; for then the bushlands above lay deep in snow, beneath which the once-lush grass and pea vine, now frozen brittle, was not worth pawing for.

They had to keep a sharp lookout in spring. The mares were heavy in foal, and all were weak till the new grass strengthened. This was the time to beware of man. At the first sign of danger, the stallion had to round them up and start them for the top, guided by the danger-wise and experienced lead-mare, urged on and kept together by the master's sudden, teeth-snapping lunges. Yearlings and two-year-old studs tended to keep a little apart; even their hot young blood dared not brave the onslaught of their sire, and the young mares were not yet for them. But they had to rejoin the herded band at a time like this, so with streaming manes and high, shrill whinnies, they, too, had to gallop up and come under the wrath of the stallion.

The Black Wolf heard the scream too. He knew the way of horses even better than the traders. He knew, too, that if you ran them, kept them moving, there was always the chance that a mare would drop behind or to one side to ease the pace for a new-born foal. If more than one did so, there was the opportunity to close in and engage one, while the stallion urged on the others. The wolf's ears puckered once or twice in his half-doze, and when he raised his snout, drops of desire fell from his jowls and splashed in the dry dust. Horse hunters—human or four-legged—had many disappointments, but in the end they had also their share of successes.

The woods were green now, fully caparisoned for summer, and the range grasses were of a height to nod in the breeze, while the wild roses from the hillside and wolf-willow from the creek banks filled the land with scent as the flickers filled it with yakking sound.

The country was the more secretive for the arch of leaves, the depth of the coulees less noticeable and therefore more treacherous. The treetops were almost level, in spite of the slope, for their trunks, tall and straight near the bottom, were a mere scrubby crooked tangle where the wind lashed hard at the top.

The red stallion's band did not feed long in the saddle. They were drifting into higher, shadier country. At this season the bush grass would be lush, and already the pea vine would be twining its tendrils about the low scrub and the whip-like saplings which had grown up since last spring's ground fire.

A buckskin mare, old and stiff, began to move away to the higher ground. One by one the band began to gather up—greys, bays, pintos, claybanks, sorrels, and blacks, some with blazes as broad as Hereford cows, some with blue "china" eyes, some with spots or stars or white stockings. Wild, free, and beautiful, they gathered with soft, half-uttered whinnies, the yearlings nipping each other or wheeling with mischievous hooves, the older mares stepping out soberly, the young mares and fillies flirting and tossing their heads.

The red stallion, full of juicy grass, began his rounds, nudging and coaxing his mares, reeling backwards with a grunt when his attentions were spurned, pressing his suit where he found the slightest encouragement or where he thought the defence might soon be lowered. A young mare, a mealy-nosed brown with a month-old foal, nickered softly, and he trotted to her, nostrils wide, prancing round her in all his pride. She nickered again, and he answered with a squeal of exultation, still curveting, till she turned; and then he reared, his red mane flashing in the sun, frightening away the foal, which bleated at this intrusion, this brief separation from its dam. With consummation came a cooling of the big horse's ardour, but not of his chivalry, for he still circled her, curving his brave neck and dipping his proud head, until they rejoined the straggling band, which now fell into single file under the dappled shadows, each stepping in the hoof-prints of the one before it.

So soft was the forest floor, so well padded the ancient game-trail, that the band moved almost silently, each forced to keep its place between the twin hedges of underbrush flanking the trail. Almost invisible were the horses too, the sun falling only in narrow bars and tiny flecks upon their glossy spring coats. They might have passed a city man within a bare fifty yards, these twenty-odd animals with over a dozen foals, and been mistaken only for sun motes and wind-stirred leaves.

At the sound or smell of danger they were prepared to halt as one, velvet nostrils wide, jewelled eyes looking all in one direction. But there was no danger today, and only once did a sound send a ripple down the line. A clumsy yearling had trodden on the protruding horn-case of a wood-bison skull and brought it to light, moss-covered yet hardly bleached from many years of lying in leaf-mold.

The bison had long ago helped to make that deep, winding water-trail, had lowered his black and shining muzzle into the pool to which it led, his comrades grunting and shoving on either side, the ripples of their intrusion making circles of quick-silver on the brown waters of this remote tarn, all shaded by dark flanking evergreens.

The bison had neither smelt nor seen the keen-faced hunter of the Beaver tribe who had levelled his Winchester from behind a fallen tangle. From this shot had come some of the last fat pemmican which, in the fall of 1912, had found its way to the Hudson's Bay post on the river, the forerunner of today's settlement. That the shot had been true was plain to see today; that round hole had drilled behind the frontal bone, under the horn, to reach the brain. But the next time the mares followed that trail, the skull was gone; the Boy, riding, following the hoof-marks, with his rifle in the crook of his arm, had found it and carried it back to camp on his lap.

The Man was interested. "That means," he said, "water for cattle on the upper range. Good. And we've a lot more riding to do, for we've got to explore thoroughly. Where there's water, cattle can graze. I don't want any of ours to be obliged to go more than a mile to drink. And thanks to the wild horses, water shouldn't be hard to find. If it's around, every trail is finally bound to lead to it. We'll call the water you found Buffalo Pool. We've got to have names for places, or we won't know what we're talking about when we want to meet or go in any certain direction looking for stock. I'm making a map with a name for every ridge, point, and creek."

The bison skull eventually found a place over the front door, where it soon bleached as white as the snows on the mountains and was used as a nesting place by two brown wrens.

The cabin of peeled logs now stood golden in the sunshine. The roof of brush and sod projected at one end over the doorway, providing a cool porch.

The hobbled horses had been caught up and harnessed; the walking-plough, which, dismembered, had been brought on the back of sturdy old Jack, was once again bolted together; and soon the sod, which had never before felt cold iron, began to fall in gleaming, chocolate-red furrows. And now the little garden—the first the Woman had, into which she had pushed many tiny seeds—began to show tiny green points of corn, the emerald of peas, and the pale yellow of the early lettuces which would grow so rapidly in this northern latitude under the impetus of warm spring rains and nights so short that darkness hardly fell before dawn again tinted the sky.

The Woman looked across the flat to where long furrows of what would be a hayfield alternated with piles of cut brush and roots. A great wave of wonder and thankfulness surged through her. Next year there would be stooks, or coils of hay, she supposed, instead of the unsightly brush piles which now billowed smoke. Below the Tumbling Hills she could hear her menfolk as they drove stakes and unrolled barbed wire to make a wrangle field—a pasture, she called it—for the horses.

For over a month the animals had grazed at night, hobbled, to be available for the morning's work. Only on Sundays had they all been turned loose with only the Boy's top saddle-horse, Mojave, kept on picket to round them up when they strayed too far. Always there had been fear of them joining a wild bunch and being temporarily lost. Breaking of land had to be done in early summer, otherwise the sod would not rot properly; and it would be a heartbreaking loss of time to have to spend perhaps three or four days riding in search of strayed horses.

There had been no time to make a fence before; the cabin came first and then the breaking—twenty acres. By tomorrow the horses would be enclosed, and no longer would she be disturbed by their thumping and banging; and she could rake and tidy up and keep the barnyard influence where it belonged—on the other side of the spruce, where already the scrub had been cut and piled to make room for a barn, a stackyard, and a branding corral.

So she stood, this woman, who had taken houses, plumbing, paved roads, and swift transportation for granted; this woman who had come from a land where it was casually remarked that this house was two hundred, that house four hundred years old; those houses which looked as much a part of the original landscape as the churchyard elms with their rooks, or the water meadows spangled with ox-eye daisies.

She had wondered how you made a home in the wilderness, how you washed, slept, ate, and took shelter. But now she knew. A house was basically tree trunks; a blanket meant sleep; a pot of beans a meal. A rifle was your butcher. A simple spring, gushing from the ground was your water tap—as wonderful as that which had flowed forth at the touch of Moses' rod. The good poplar wood needed no stove. It burnt with as clear a flame in the neat rock fireplace, boiled the tea water as inevitably as any stove. It had only to be cut and split.

This, she thought, was how the Bushmen of Africa, the Mongol herders of the Gobi, and the explorers and pioneers of her own race, had managed. Everything needed was at hand. Gradually things had taken shape. The Man had told her: "There's nothing to it. We can be as comfortable as in the best hotel!"

She hadn't quite understood then but had fallen back on faith. He had always seemed to know what was needed and how to do things. Whatever crisis had threatened, he had always been able to produce the palliative from the packs. Once it had been a surgical needle and a suture. With this he had drawn together the jagged tear in the Kid's leg that time the youngster had stumbled against a sharp, new-cut stump. Next time it had been coloured packets of garden seed. Tomorrow it might be a can of pine-tar to treat the snagged wound in a horse's frog.

Now she sat at the cabin door, nursing the cat and musing on three great blessings. Her man and the boys. Her little house and garden. And the new life quickening beneath her heart.

She picked up her sewing.

Chapter 4

All through the day the Cow Moose heard the axes and the talking. She was deep in the shade and knew she had only to stand still, keep her calves lying quietly, and whatever it was would pass by. But they didn't move very fast, these two-legged creatures, and her anxiety grew. She had no reason to leave the cool, shady bower which sheltered her. She fed at night under the sickle moon, when the shrubbery was cool and wet with dew, leaving the edge of the willows only to make one nightly visit to drink at the creek four hundred yards to the west.

This night the noises had ceased, and she felt safe again. She started across to the creek, flitting like a ghost, leaving her twins couched like stones. Once a horned owl lit above them. It was rabbits he hunted that night, and even to his night-eyes there was nothing to suggest that there was living, breathing life in the moon-cast shadows.

The Cow Moose drank. The wind was in the east. No danger-scent came to her nostrils as she tested the air this way and that, as the water trickled from her great velvety lip. Once she heard a jingle and a thump, and she turned her ungainly head, so full of primitive beauty, her ears forward. Then silence, except for the oily lap of water against the bank. The sound came again. She stood, still as a tree. Then a cranky squeal and the thud of a kick.

The Man's horses—that was all. Young Romeo had grazed too close to Ginger, and now his ribs ached for his temerity. The Cow Moose had known horses ever since she was a calf. She had drunk from one side of a forest pool, even as a band of mares had slaked their thirst on the other.

She knew, too, that horses were more afraid of her than she of them. For she was of old sib to this ancient, scarred, and shaggy land, to which horses were but newcomers of the last hundred years or so. She knew that, should they scent her, they would stand and stare, making ready to run and blowing loud blasts through their nostrils. The Man, too, knew those explosive blasts. How often had they wakened the sleepers in their tent. How often had he murmured: "Go back to sleep. It's only the horses. Probably a moose around."

The Black Wolf knew something too. That Betsy, the brown mare, would soon foal. Tonight he made the rounds of the little bunch of tame horses. He was suspicious of the thumps and jingles. It would not be easy to steal a foal from this bunch, he thought—when if he had known it, hobbled horses are the least able to fight back or flee.

The Black Wolf satisfied himself that Betsy had not yet foaled. When she was ready, she would move aside, and then, perhaps . . .

As he slipped through the shadows, the wolf came in line with the little breeze flowing from him to the creek, towards the Cow Moose. Her nose spoke to her.

This was something different from horses, and the big animal angled across the flat like a shadow, to stand once more by her calves. The wolf had not seen, heard, or smelt her, yet nevertheless his hackles rose and he trotted to a low knoll, raised his muzzle, and howled in the eerie, reverberating downward scale of his kind. The horses trumpeted through their nostrils and began to clump noisily towards the camp.

"That was no moose, that was a wolf," said the wakened Man. "But don't worry—it's not likely they'll bother our stock for a while, anyway. There's plenty of other game."

But this was his first intimation that wolves were so close, and next day he said to the Boy: "We'd best get that fence finished, or we may have the horses run off. A new fence won't look good to a timber wolf—not till he gets used to the look and smell of it. Wish we could find their den—they're bound to have one. But it may be miles away, since wolves hunt on a big circuit. Anyway, I went over by the creek this morning and got his pad-marks. He's a big fellow."

The Boy counted out his 30-30 shells that night. A box and a half—that should do for a while.

And the Kid, as he rolled in his blankets, said: "A wolf, eh?" and went to sleep.

The new pasture was almost finished. The sun was getting high, and it was hot in the shelter of the Tumbling Hills. The Boy was driving posts and stretching wire with the help of the Kid, who carried tools, fetched water for his thirsty brother, and helped to line up the posts. Soon the last of the wire would be stretched and fastened. While his sons were thus engaged, the Man began to hew out a water trough from a new-felled cottonwood, one of several that sucked up the spring-water to nourish their dark, glossy leaves. This trough would go on the north side of the spring, separated from the water by poles, so that the horses would not foul the water, or the Man be crowded when dipping his pail.

The sweat poured from him, and he left his work to walk north along the new fence-line. The wire was up on three sides; that precious wire which had been packed on the stout backs of old Ginger and young Romeo; the first, for all his grizzled age and his Pan-like beard, carrying it with a swagger; the younger horse, still leggy and inexperienced, hating his pack but still ready to follow where old Ginger led. Now all that remained was eighty rods separating the barnyard from the northeast corner.

Most of the posts were in, and the Man passed the Kid sharpening pickets for the last short gap. The Boy was up ahead, stretching wire, but out of sight beyond a rise of ground.

The Man heard the stretcher, put his hand to the wire to feel the tension, and called to the Boy that it was tight enough. The squeal of the stretcher ceased, and the Boy threw a couple of half-hitches around a post and began stapling, the tap-tap of his hammer ringing sharply in the bush.

Suddenly there was a movement and noise, the crash of dry

willows, and a dark form loomed monstrously as it pushed through the thicket, followed by two gangling foal-like creatures with big ears. They passed the end of the wire at a trot and disappeared up the hill.

"Gosh!" said the Boy. "Almost ran over me! That's the old cow moose, and she's got two calves. Guess she didn't want to be fenced in. Good thing she made it, or she'd have bust the wire!"

The Kid looked at the tracks. "Some meat there," he said in his solemn way.

They all laughed.

"Well, come on!" the Man finally said. "Dinner should be ready. Don't know about you fellows, but I'm hungry enough to eat the tail-bone of a coyote!"

The Black Wolf's wife also heard the screech of tightening wire and the blows of the post-mall, muffled by two miles' distance.

The puppies, which had been nursing, relaxed their hold on her teats one by one and lay sprawled out, fat-bellied, snoring slightly. Softly the bitch left the den, feeling for scent this way and that with her wet nose. She struggled out into daylight and slipped silently to the creek. Here she bent her head and lapped at the water which flowed over the gravel bar.

Refreshed, she silently limped her way uphill, until from between the stems of a willow she could look across the valley to where the white tent and the pale yellow cabin stood outlined against the leafy willows and dark green spruces.

She had seen the Woman in the dooryard, and now could see the three males of the establishment walking, axes glinting on shoulders, to the campfire. In spite of the distance she also saw some small animal which moved like a fox but jumped without fear into the Woman's lap.

The three-footed wolf growled, the mere whisper of a growl, expressing herself more in a movement of her corded throat than by any real sound. And she looked down at where her left paw should be, licking the stump of her wrist-joint, as she had licked it at intervals for over three years, as if with the caress she might somehow see a new paw there. That loss was, she knew, a symbol of the pain which was brother to the man-smell.

She still vividly remembered how she had lost that paw.

. . . Again in her mind she was quietly hunting along an ancient trail, when, suddenly, she felt herself held by that Thing of metal, hidden so treacherously beneath the dust.

She could not escape from It, and each struggling effort to do so brought such pain that she howled anguish, across the star-drenched hillside.

She lacerated her gums and broke a tooth on the Thing but to no avail; in the end she gave up the struggle and drew back on her haunches to lie motionless in the silence and darkness.

Terrified, her leg burning with a pain which seemed about to reach and still her thumping heart, she seemed, for this moment, to be utterly alone: And she howled again. This time she heard her mate's hoarse answer.

Then all at once the Black Wolf was beside her. One lick to her ear, and he was down like a dog to a bone. He clamped his vice-like jaws around the leg, above the trap-jaws. His mate felt the searing pain as sinew, flesh, and bone were sliced and crunched. The pain set her hackles up, her ears flat to her head, and her eyes closed so tightly that all she could see was the colour, the texture of her red and sleekly velvety agony.

Then she was free. He turned, and never stopping for a look or a lick, she loped three-legged in his wake. Her pups of that year were still within her and would be for some weeks yet, but they must have a home.

The smell of metal, a smell never to be forgotten, was rank in their nostrils as the two wolves left behind them for ever the place of Iron and the river. Following the gullied badlands and the sidehills of Cutbank Creek, they travelled the rest of the night, north and west.

Dawn was breaking when the Black Wolf paused above a high point. He waited for his mate to reach his side, then led her down to the mouth of the den where he himself had first drawn breath . . .

Somehow the sight of the Woman and her menfolk brought back these memories. With the growl still half-uttered in her throat, the bitch returned to her puppies.

Chapter 5

The pack-horses were milling and dodging within the newly built corral. The Boy threw a skilful rope and brought a pinto to a standstill.

"Halter, Dad!" he called. The Man coaxed the leather over reluctant ears and tied the horse, as the Boy made another catching-loop. Soon eight pack-animals, including the bearded Ginger and white-stockinged old Jack, stood tied in a line.

The Boy and his father were preparing the horses for a trip to the settlement, for the pack-horses were needed to carry supplies. Some of them would need to have their feet trimmed, while halters, pack-saddles, and gear would have to be repaired and oiled, and lash ropes and block cinches would have to be put ship-shape.

"Who's going with you?" queried the Boy.

"You," was the reply. "We'll have big loads. The main thing is more barbed wire. We'll have to fence the breaking. No use putting in a crop next year and letting wild horses and our own cattle tromp it into the ground. We'll have to get busy next year and brush out the trail and do some work on it, so we can get in seed grain and lumber for the house. If we get that fencing done beforehand we won't be held up then. I think the Kid will manage to help Mother while we're gone. So let's get the pack-saddles and put our grub and blankets on old Jack."

The Woman watched them out of sight. Supplies were running short. No rice, only a few beans, a few spoonfuls of tea and no more than a pound of sugar remained. She had enough flour for another baking, and some venison still hung in the spring-crib. Lucky they had that. Men can't work without meat, and only last week she had put a pair of spurs on the Boy's plate, and he had known what that meant: The corned beef and the bacon were finished. The golden leaves were falling and the nights were frosty, but it had been still too warm to kill a moose; they all knew that.

She had been happy when the Boy had come back that evening with a fat black-tailed buck. The Man had called it a mule deer, but Seton Thompson in her favourite childhood book had always written of them as "black-tails"—"the bounding black-tails." And bound they did, like rubber balls, when suddenly surprised in the hills.

The Woman felt no sense of loneliness. She was far too busy. And she had the Kid, who did his chores faithfully. He weeded the garden, changed Robin's picket-rope twice a day, and brought her wood and water. It was he who rose early to light the fire and to make tea in his own peculiar way; tip-toeing into the tent to set down her cup, and then retreating shyly. How kind he always was, yet how uncommunicative. Not like the Boy—really a man—who plumped himself down by the spruce-bough bed and chattered of his horse or his rifle, or discussed the chaps and spurs in Riley and McCormick's catalogue as if she were another young cowboy!

The Woman loved her daily walks, although they were short ones. The fall crop of wild berries had brought many bears into the valley. Some were black, some red, some pale cinnamon, some large, some medium-sized. But the Man told her they were all one kind and explained the colour phases as an example of what he called bi-chromatism. Sometimes she saw a mother bear with cubs, and did as she had been told—walked quietly in another direction.

You never knew what you might see—or imagine you saw—in this queer country. In England, where everything was neat, a thing was recognizable for what it was. But here the dark hollows in the bush, the shade cast by a rock, a gnarled tree trunk caught in a patch of sunlight, might be anything, might harbour anything. A piece of blackened, burnt deadfall log would even *move* if you looked at it long enough!

These men of hers could certainly eat meat, and the Woman, as she sliced some for dinner, thought of "collops of red deer's flesh," and smiled to herself. How like the life of seventeenth-century England was this semi-primitive existence here in the twentieth! No wonder her thoughts went to *Lorna Doone* with its descriptions of pack-horses, of herds of sheep lost on lonely moorlands, of kitchens with open fires. How like to the life of Plover's Barrows farm was this daily round of hers. This great, lonely country was a little bit like the Exmoor of those days, where never a car-track showed. A letter from London took a long time to reach John Ridd's home, just like here. It had to be passed from hand to hand. The only mail she had seen since early spring was a packet brought by one of the horse traders. Careless they might be, these doughty riders with their wind-tanned faces and dark eyes; careless when it came to brands, ready to claim any horse on the range; but they had their own brittle, twisted sense of honour—like Sir Ensor Doone—and a letter or a woman was safe in their care.

That time she thought she saw a radio-tower glinting like a thing of metal on the ridge, and wondered how it got there. . . . It was a bleached old birch tree, shining against a dark and stormy sky!

Now, with the leaves falling and the bush becoming grey, purple, and blue in the distance, strange shapes loomed up everywhere. She, used to looking across a ten-acre field, from hedgerow to hedgerow, found it hard to judge distance. Was that clump of spruce really two miles away, as the Man had told her? It still seemed to her that she could walk to it in five minutes. She comforted herself by thinking of the Man's admission that he, too, had the same difficulty, after all his years.

Once, following a faint game-trail across the Tumbling Hills, she heard a rustle. She stood still. *She* wasn't afraid of a good-natured old bear, but yet. . . . There had been rumours of a grizzly. Old Atchikoos had seen a track west of Big Prairie. And old Atchikoos, she well knew, was one of the best hunters among the little band of Beaver Indians whose camp was fifty miles north-west at the Crying Girl Prairie. The man had said so.

Her thoughts were interrupted by a movement ahead. Some animal—yes. It was a very small bear waddling away, a greenish-brown one! Only it wasn't a bear at all, but a fat porcupine, and she laughed. And at that the solemn creature squatted in the path—it wasn't fifteen feet away—and stood, all its striped quills on end. She returned to the cabin, and the Kid heard her and said politely: "Porcupine, eh?" and thereafter that path was called the Porcupine Trail.

The Woman suddenly realized that all the old safe and familiar places in England must have been named the same way years ago! Some Saxon woman noticed, perhaps, a red-ochre outcrop in a stream's bank, and so was born Redditch. As she prepared dinner, the Woman amused herself by trying to remember these names—Blackpool, Ramsgate, Crowborough, yes, and Starvecrow Field on her uncle's farm; so why not Deep Springs, Moose Point, and Porcupine Trail? Once named, mysterious and strange places took on another, more orderly atmosphere.

Altogether, this life broadened the mind by a new approach and caused one to make a more direct evaluation of one's surroundings. She thought of her father's hunters, of her own mount, little Titmouse, who could take a fence as well as any of them. Yet she had never appreciated them as she now did shaggy little Ginger and sure-footed Robin. These were not ridden for fun, she realized. They were part of you, as your legs were part of you.

When all was named, all was mapped, all was safe and secure, something would be lost. Perhaps uncertainty, not taking things for granted, helped one to live more fully.

Quite often Lillian, the little grey cat, came with her on these walks. She was company, somehow. Lillian had been named by the Kid from a favourite book of his by Damon Runyon. She came from the settlement, in which for some reason nearly all the cats were grey with white paws and were extremely well-behaved. The Woman called them Peace River cats. Lillian's bêtes noires were the short-eared owls which nested in the scrubby tangles of long grass and willows on the flat. Whenever her mistress walked in that direction, the owls would circle overhead and Lillian would run to the Woman's skirts for protection. So, with the cat in her arms, together with a bunch

of late Michaelmas daisies and scarlet leaves, she would return to the cabin, while the owls settled down.

The warm weather broke on the third day that the men were away. The wind swept down the valley from the north with wild ferocity, making the tall spruce by the barn sway and groan in eerie accents. The Kid had to tighten the tent-pegs, and Robin had to be repicketed in a more sheltered spot. Lillian, who in anticipation of the storm had raced around the cabin and up one tree after another, now lay sleeping under the bunk, against the cabin wall.

The fallen leaves became sodden. The wind sent several dead trees crashing to earth with such a noise that the sleeping cat twitched her ears and the grass bent like grain before the reaping-hook.

On the fourth day the wind began to die down and a pale sun showed itself briefly above the cloud-rack in the west, behind which the mountain peaks crouched in obscurity. Summer was on its way out, and the fall was here. There was a chill in the air. Well, perhaps it would clear up and stay nice till Christmas—it sometimes did. Or it might rain or snow, and thaw and snow again, till freeze-up, though it was only October.

At dusk the Woman and the Kid, listening, heard voices and then the jingling tramp of the pack-train. Robin snorted, then whinnied, as through the damp and chill the caravan loomed up strangely, formlessly, like willows bending in a mist. Soon the yard was full of tramping hooves and tired voices.

The Woman had asked the Kid to light a lantern, and now, as he held it high, she saw the white-blazed, amiable face of Fox, and Mojave's tossing head—for that horse never admitted fatigue, but would rather have dropped dead in his tracks.

"Tell your father a hot supper's ready," she called.

The Man shouted. "Lots of time! We'll have to get these packs unloaded and everything covered with tarps!"

It seemed ages before the last horse was turned into the wrangle field. Muddied and bedraggled they threw themselves down to roll, and the Woman could hear their grunts and the clicking of their hooves, and the shuddering sound as they rose and shook themselves, then the slow hoof-beats and the tearing sound as they grazed. Robin whinnied again from his picket-rope, but there was no answer from the tired pack-string.

The Man came in, muddy, gaunt, unshaven, and shivering a little, taking off his canvas jacket as he warmed at the little fire. Smiling, he laid the mail on the table. The Boy was still fussing over some gear, hanging up pack-saddles and coiling ropes.

They sat down to venison stew, all talking at once, laughing too. People do, when they are tired in body from battling long miles, or when they have been listening anxiously for the clink of a bridle or the thump of a hoof.

As the Woman began to open the mail, Lillian crept from beneath the bunk, deftly avoided the spurred and muddied boot heels, and called loudly for scraps.

Chapter 6

Sure enough, the damp, cold weather was followed by six weeks of Indian summer, during which they went to work fencing and then cutting enough fifty-foot spruce logs for a permanent home. The men had to go across the creek and around Wild Horse Point—a matter of over two miles—to reach the nearest grove of tall, straight spruce. They went with teams, for they would need horses to "snake" the logs into piles. On arrival, the horses were unhitched and tied to trees for the time being. The Man wandered through the dark aisles, looking upward from the base of each tree in turn, to gauge their straightness, for many had crooks halfway up. He deftly blazed with his axe each tree that passed this scrutiny, until, satisfied he had marked enough, he joined the Boy, whose axe was already starting to ring.

The Kid made himself useful in many ways. He helped to trim the fallen giants with a hand axe; he brought lunch at noon; and he was constantly back and forth with water for the axemen, for it was hot and windless in the bush.

Later he and his brother led one of the patient, knowing horses, standing at their heads while the Man hooked the heavy log-chain around each smooth butt in turn. This done, his terse "O.K." would start up the horse. It was the Boy's or the Kid's job to select the best route between the standing trees and stumps to prevent the log jamming. Sometimes that happened, bringing the horse to a grunting stop. Then whoever led the horse had to take a peavy hewn from a small tree, and roll the log free once more.

The gruelling work went on for three days, the last of which was spent peeling the bark from the logs—"skinning logs," they said, in the parlance of the country.

These now lay in piles of twelve to twenty at the edge of their trail, well peeled and glowing golden in the sun of early winter.

But the baby was due to come soon, and the cramped quarters of the little cabin would not do for four people to winter in, and other plans had been made.

Daylight dawned after a warm and windless night to reveal the tent sagged down by six inches of snow. The mountains were again obscured, but as the sun rose the clouds parted and the distant peaks shone for a moment, coral pink. Then the curtain dropped again—except in the north-west, where a patch of dull, duck-egg green glowed malevolently. The Man knew the sign. More snow and cold winds coming.

"Time to get going," said the Man.

They were ready. Horses were saddled, packs adjusted, and the little party started for the settlement, where the Man and the Boy had work for the winter.

Within two days the valley showed no sign of its recent occupancy. Even the cabin was now no more than a snow-covered mound. The whisky-jacks picked around the doorstep but found no crumbs or scraps.

The Black Wolf from the ridgetop gazed with deep satisfaction upon the deserted yard. Even the dark patch of breaking which had been turned over that summer was deep in snow and showed no sign of its disturbance by the plough, now lying abandoned at the furrow's end, only its curved handles showing above the drifts.

It was the end of March before the Black Wolf again encountered the man-smell. Trotting north on his lawful business, he raised his hackles at the sight of a fresh sleigh-trail in the deep snow. He touched his nose to it and knew the answer. The Man had come again.

He had come, taking advantage of warmer weather and longer days to haul the logs the two miles to Deep Springs. He would have to hurry, too, to get the job done before the snow melted under the chinook which now blew fitfully from the west. No wagon could as yet reach the valley, but sleighs can go where wagons cannot. Soft ground is frozen hard in winter, and runners are narrow, can turn more sharply, and are able to wind between trees which would impede a wagon's wider-set wheels. The frozen creeks, too, were deep in snow, the deadfalls were so covered that they no longer impeded, and the whole country lay smooth beneath the white blanket.

The Man lit the stove in the cabin—the little Daisy range—and arranged the supplies he had brought. Tea, sugar, beans, salt pork, and flour for bannock. Also he had brought sacked oats for his horses. For hay he had a small mound in the corral cut last summer with a scythe in a small meadow among the willows half a mile to the west. He had dragged this hay there on a home-made stone-boat, a thing of two hewn runners with cross-bars of small poles. To his satisfaction he found the small stack undisturbed and crisply green under its covering of snow.

It was a hard job breaking the trail to the logs, but the Man noted with delight that the crossing at Wild Horse Creek was drifted deep in snow and looked not nearly so formidable as in summer. After a few trips he had a good trail, so that the horses' hooves crunched pleasantly in the morning frost and the sleigh followed easily. Only two logs the first load; then four; after which he loaded six or even seven, the hind runners let out with an eight-foot log-chain—in spite of which the long ends of the logs dragged, and once the outfit nearly upset when an extra-long one caught against a tree as he was making the sharp downward turn to cross the crooked little creek. That could have spelled death, for he was in danger of being caught underneath if the bunk-stakes broke and the logs rolled. But they held, and as the heaving horses struggled up the far bank and the sleigh levelled out, the Man wiped his face with the red and white handkerchief which always showed a corner from the hip pocket of his overalls.

In four days the job was done—just as the snow, melting rapidly under the now-steady roar of the chinook, had become so shallow that the sleigh began to cut through to the ground beneath. Another load would have stalled the horses.

The Man, as he rolled the logs to the ground, arranging them neatly with a peavy-pole, was not sorry the job was over. He had been obliged to shovel the snow from the piles in the bush, and they had been wet and slippery. To load big logs single-handed was not easy. He had to roll them up leaning poles, one end at a time, always tying the high end with a halter-rope. One slip, he knew, and a log could have crushed him, caved in his ribs perhaps, or broken a leg or arm. So it had been slow work, every movement studied, every tie-knot calculated. His legs ached, and his back. He sucked a knuckle, where he'd knocked the bark off . . .

Next morning, leaving the sleighs by the cabin, the Man put both harnesses on one horse, leaped bareback on the other, and started back for the settlement sixty crooked miles away.

The baby, already three months old, was fat and strong.

He had dubbed her "Small"—for she was a girl, as he had hoped. The family could return now, or at least as soon as green grass showed. This time they would bring up the twenty cows they had bought, and an Angus bull, the nucleus of a future herd.

And surely green grass could not be far away, the Man thought as he turned the corner of Moose Point, which was already bare of snow and smelling of good frost-free earth at last. It was the third of April. Looking west to the mountains he saw no sign of a change of weather. The great arch hung high above them. The chinook, redolent of the Pacific, was playing its usual fine-weather tricks, and he saw the jumbled peaks in a mirage, their sharp crests sliced off and moved away from their bases by the meeting of warm and cold air currents. It made him think of the Carmelhan at anchor, and

Valdemar Victorious,
Who looketh in disdain
To see his image in the tide,
Dismembered, float from side to side
And reunite again.

Those wonderful mountains! Smoking like Sinai in summer, skipping like rams these early spring mornings.

As he passed the buttes on his left, he put up a troop of wild mares. They looked thin and shaggy in the spring sunshine, and he wondered, as always, at their hardiness.

At the crossing on Thunder Creek he found the water pretty high but presenting no difficulty. The trail still followed the bench between the bank of the now easterly flowing river on his right and the higher ridges to his left, but ten miles farther these ridges crowded into the bank, leaving no room for the trail, which now dropped down into the actual valley, only climbing out again at Jasper's house. So crooked was the course of the creek and so narrow was this valley, that each loop washed the steep bank of this side or that. Three of these loops had to be forded, and these might be much deeper and more difficult than the one he had just crossed, for the sun was getting hot and he could hear the roar of released waters more loudly at each mile.

It was evening but still fairly light when he began to drop down into that dim valley, so wild, so buttressed and eroded; a fit place only for the eagles, which reared their hook-beaked young on the precipitous crags above. Before ever he started down that tortuous trail, he knew the creek was racing; he heard the sullen roar of the snow-swollen water.

It felt chilly in the gloom of the bottomland spruce. He sat his horse and gazed at the green-brown flood which tore past, fretting at the banks and undermining the flooded trees, some of which had already fallen crest-down in the current.

The Man looked at the sky above the dark spires of evergreens. The wind had dropped, and it was cloudless. It would freeze tonight. With any luck the creek would have shrunk considerably by morning. This was surface water only, as yet, flowing over the ice—but the more dangerous for that, as the footing would not be good.

Quickly he decided. He would camp for the night and try the crossing tomorrow early. He turned the horses loose. He knew by their actions that they had no wish to enter that swollen torrent, and they would find plenty of goose-grass—strong feed—beneath the spruce. He had his blankets, his tea pail, and half a bannock.

He rose early, stamped the chill out of his feet, and caught up the horses. The one he was riding refused to cross. Although

the water was down a foot or more, it still roared around the bend in such spuming fury that the animal reared and reared again, slipping dangerously on the ice it could not see. After all, he was no saddle-horse, just a plough-beast. Old Fox would have carried him over without hesitation, stepping slowly, carefully, and calmly.

One fallen spruce almost spanning the torrent gave the Man an idea. Letting go of the horse he had been riding, he grasped the lead-rope of its mate, an old mare. Coaxing and pulling gently, he got her front feet in the water, and then, straddling the tree trunk, edged forward till the rope was tight, then pulled again. The mare was in three feet of water now, trash and spume gathering against her knees. She tried to pull back, but the Man calmed her, scratching her between the ears, and she took another few steps, gingerly. She reared as, released from the impediment of the spruce the full force of the current struck her shoulder. But he was ready, with a broken spruce-branch in his other hand. As she reared, he threw the rope loose, whacking her quarters with the brittle club so that it broke with a loud crack. The mare plunged straight ahead, fell under, but righted herself, and in a few more plunges drew herself up the far bank, dripping and blowing. She whickered, and without a moment's hesitation the gelding, too, plunged in and crossed. Together they disappeared around a corner of the trail, the mare's double load of harness jingling.

The Man crept along the log towards where its broken top disappeared beneath the swirling rush of water. It was five feet to shore, and an upward jump to the top of a bank so steep that he must clear it or fall back in the creek. He did not look at the water, knowing that it would make him feel as if he were drifting sideways. Summoning all his strength he made the leap, landing on one knee on the top of the bank, which crumbled beneath him; but his right hand found the sapling he had kept his eyes on, and he drew himself up without having wet his feet.

He walked on down the trail, not worrying. He knew the horses would stop, for a while anyway, at the next ford. That was where he found them, plucking at the hollow-stemmed goose-grass.

This time he mounted the gelding again, turning the mare loose ahead of him, and because the homing instinct was now strong in her, she led the way, and they crossed the other fords without trouble.

That night, hungry, muddy, and very tired, they arrived home.

When the Woman heard that the logs were hauled she was pleased and said: "I can't wait for us all to go up."

But the Man replied: "Creeks are pretty high. We'd best wait a week, anyway," and told her about the crossings.

"Mercy me!" she cried. "You might have been hurt!"

All he said was: "People are doing that every day—think of old Atchikoos—why, he's never even *seen* a bridge, I don't suppose."

There would be lots to do before they left. The pack-horses would need their feet trimmed, the cows would have to be gathered up so they could all go together. Grub and supplies would have to be packed.

It seemed a tall order, but she knew it would all be accomplished.

She would have to ride with Small. Well, what the Indian women could do shouldn't be impossible for her. She would make a bag in a blanket and carry the baby on her back.

It was rather fun, really . . .

Chapter 7

Within two weeks the grass was strong, the south slopes and shoulders of the ridges washed with blue as the blades of wild rye-grass pushed upward. The foot of the buttes and the steep sides of Moose Ridge were dotted with fragile prairie crocuses. The willow-brakes were fragrant with golden pussy-mittens, among which the newly arrived juncos and tree sparrows hopped and chirruped.

In the soft mud left by the receding waters of Burnt Creek were fresh bear-tracks; nor were these the only signs left by their owner, for anthill after anthill had been torn open, and every old blackened log overturned for the grubs and beetles beneath.

There was no time now to get at building the house. That would have to wait, and the boys would have to use the tent, while the Woman and the child now occupied the cabin.

There was the crop to put in, which meant a trip for seed grain. The nearest settler, twelve miles to the east, had grown good oats last year, and now he consented to sell enough for their needs, obligingly hauling it on a rough wagon-road to Thunder Creek, where the Man and the Boy met him to take it the rest of the way on pack-horses.

Yet the house did get started, because just as the grain was ready there came a week of wet weather which made the land too soggy to harrow. So they set to work to put up the four walls, which would be twelve logs high by thirty feet wide and twenty feet long.

The first two "rounds"—of eight-logs—were put into place quite easily, but thereafter two slanting poles were placed against the top log. The next log would be rolled up to these poles. The Boy, with a lariat fastened to his saddle-horn, then rode to the far side and threw his rope across both walls. The Man had to put the rope around the log, then take it back to fasten on the bottom log of the far side. He then signalled to the Boy, who touched his horse with the spur. The forward movement caused the bight of the rope—in which the log now lay—to roll the log up the poles until its ends rested on the cross-logs. It could then be manoeuvred into any position. In morticing to the cross-logs, the Man and the Boy worked one at each end, and at the same time. A good mortice made a good corner, and except for a plumb-line to keep the corner vertical, they needed no other tools than their axes and swede saws, although for pinning a crooked log a wood auger was desirable, as well as a couple of draw-knives.

From the ridge came the stamping and clucking of the wild prairie chickens. Each morning they gathered in hundreds on their ancient dance-grounds. Sometimes the Kid crept up a shadowed coulee to look over the rim to watch their mating dances, the sparring tournaments of the males, with their stamping and circling, while the sober hens looked on. He was often so close that he could see the birds' distended air-sacs and the yellow spring combs above their eyes.

But this morning it was a big red fox who watched the shuffling, noisy birds. The fox took two, three steps, belly to the ground. He knew how to make that final rush. He knew that from among the startled, fluttering grouse he was sure to be able to seize one in his narrow, toothed jaws. At the moment he tensed for the onslaught, he heard a strange, high, drawn-out crow—something he had never heard before. He backed up, turned, and loped away like a wind-blown leaf.

So Chanticleer, the gallant defender of his Pertelots, unwittingly saved the life of a wild cousin.

Again the Cow Moose felt the urge of spring. All winter,

never far from her kind, she had browsed among the alders and the tall mountain willows of the ridge—those willows which now showed stark, broken-down boughs which would never leaf again from their stripped and wounded terminal twigs. Among those willows lay many cast antlers of bulls, some old and half-buried, some new and already gleaming whitely, all with their tine-tips chewed by porcupines hungry for calcium. And among the antlers, mound after small scattered mound of the tight, golden nutmegs, which are moose's dung.

Again she left the high country for the solitude she longed for. This time her calves of the previous year were not with her. One had made a meal for the wolves. The other, stricken with ticks, was already so emaciated that it had no will to follow. Only a heavy rain could save it, make the gorged ticks drop to the ground, and allow its neck—all rubbed and raw, stiff with parasites—to "hair-over" again. The moose approached the fence warily. Once, during the early winter, a bull, coming to her call from across the valley, had blundered into it, snapping the wire and breaking off several posts. But the Man had repaired the break before turning out Starlight, the little brown saddle-horse and Julie, the bay brood-mare and her golden yearling and her two-year-old buckskin with the frozen ears.

Following the pasture fence the moose saw nothing of those horses, although two days before they had been plain to be seen, grazing quietly, from the ridge above. Then she paused. Was that man-smell? She couldn't be sure. It was stale. There was little to fear if man had but passed that way. Then she saw that the wires were again broken, hanging loose between two posts. Easily she stepped between and silently entered the deep willow grove of her former maternity.

The Man rode down the pasture field in the dewy morn. A ruffed grouse drummed from the poplars. A marsh hawk floated overhead, a male he thought, blue as a gull above, the white of its rump gleaming in the sun.

Where the dickens were those horses? He needed the field now for the work-stock, and planned to turn out the idle ones onto the range west of the crop fence, where they could more easily be watched, since they would be in view of the house most of the time. They had no inclination to go south, and the west and north were blocked by Cutbank Creek on the north-west—here very swift—and the deep canyon of Wild Horse Creek on the north.

He checked Fox, who whinnied, as he always did on his favourite job, looking for horses. No soft, muttered answer came. No ringing of a horse-bell. Well, sometimes they went into the willows, sneakily, and stood still, so Julie's bell would not clang. He couldn't ride in there. But he had often gone in on foot and by bending low had been able to see their legs. Then he had chased them out as a dog might, and mounted Fox to follow them.

There they were—the sly devils! Legs moving! He crouched low and crept closer, then raised a little to shout, as he always did. But the shout froze on his lips. Between the interlaced boughs above those half-seen legs, he stared into the face of the Cow Moose, who, with lowered head and raised neck-bristles, stood over her still-wet, droop-eared calf, which at that moment gave something between a sneeze and a bleat. The man backed up, chuckling.

Mounted again, he rode around the fence and found the break. He gazed at it long and thoughtfully. A clean cut, and no posts broken. Looked like a fence-plier job. Tracks of horses passing through, up the hill. He followed. Then he saw what told the tale as clear as print. A scattering of horse dung, such as is made by a galloping horse—not the dark green and chocolate dung of range or pastured horses feeding on old grass mixed with new. This was bright yellow, like oat straw, and speckled with white, half-chewed grain.

A saddle-horse. Not one of his own, he knew. A fed, a "grained" saddle-horse, such as you need to run wild horses if you are to outdistance them.

Those horse traders, he thought at once. They wouldn't want the pensioned-off old gelding, Starlight; but they couldn't leave him behind to run the fence and whinny all night.

For almost two days, with black suspicion eating their hearts, the Man and the Boy followed that trail. It was slow work, for so many wild-horse tracks criss-crossed. The trail went due east, across Thunder Creek, beyond which a sudden thunderstorm mixed with hail had wiped away all hoof-marks as if they had never been, flattening the grass and scouring the open burnt ground. It seemed useless to go farther. The general direction led towards the new Yukon Highway, but there was a big country in between. Only last winter the Man had heard rumours of hidden corrals in the bush, just out of sight of that road, and of trucks which stopped at night. But no one had seen them.

Rumours. You can't waste time on rumours. You'd best forget them. Either the horses were already out of the country, or if they had eluded their captors—and old Starlight knew all the tricks—they would work their way home.

Old Atchikoos and his squaw were on their way to the stampede and horse-races at the settlement. The Beaver clansman sat straight on his ewe-necked buckskin. As the little party followed the top of the West Fork sidehills his old eyes—keen as ever—saw the shadow which dropped in a flash behind Wolf Point. Quickly, throwing his trail-rope to Old Mary, he slipped his rifle from its scabbard and stealthily pigeon-toed towards the brow of the cliff, his moccasins noiseless on the brittle grass. Prone now, he inched his way forward till he could command a view of the valley below. But the extreme base of the point was still hidden from view. His nostrils flared below his thin nose and alert eyes. A wolf skin brought twenty-five dollars' bounty at the agent's office, and probably another ten at the Jew's store in the settlement!

For perhaps five minutes Atchikoos lay thus. Then with a grunt he raised himself and clambered around the steep shoulder of the cliff. It was fifteen minutes before he reappeared and made his way to Mary, who was sitting motionless on a stump and holding the horses.

"Wolf den!" said the Indian. Mary nodded.

Rapidly, in the clicking tones of the Beaver tribe, Atchikoos told his plan. He had found the den. The shadow had entered it. There was, he had heard, a new white man beyond the forks, across the cutbank, at the springs below Moose Ridge. Even up beyond the Butler Range, on the Crying Girl Prairie, he had heard this. The man had cattle, so he would not like wolves. Also, he would have shovels or spades.

"I shall go to the white man," Atchikoos said. "Borrow some tools and return to dig out the pups. I have seen their sign at the den-mouth. Maybe get a shot at the old ones."

Even the pups would fetch a tidy sum, and Mary nodded, thinking of a new silk shawl from the company man.

"You stay," he finished. "Watch. Spring is getting old, maybe they will move. They know I was there." He galloped off.

The squaw hobbled the saddle-beasts and the pack-horse, letting them graze as she seated herself stoically on the point, watching, watching. . . . She did not go down to the den. Her legs were sore and swollen since last winter's influenza.

She did not know that, from the den, an unseen, narrow gully dropped to the bottom and around the shoulder of the cliff, ending in a tangled willow-brake.

Within an hour Old Atchikoos returned, drumming with his heels on his horse's ribs, while the animal still heaved and puffed after the climb from the cutbank crossing.

The Man was with him, and the Boy. Down the steep slope they half ran, half slid, Atchikoos in the lead. But at the den's mouth were fresh tracks, many tracks. It looked bad. Nevertheless the men dug out the den till the Indian, by thrusting in a lissom and twiggy branch, could feel the end. Twist the branch as he might, he felt nothing; nor, when he withdrew it, could he find a trace of wolf hair clinging.

"Wolf gone," was all he said, as he straightened his old back. "All gone. Old woman he eye no good. Mebbeso wolf leavum, right away I go. Mebbeso too big. Spring-time stay." And he grinned, showing the few yellow fangs in his shrunken gums.

"Better come eat," said the Man, and the Beaver signed to Mary as he mounted.

They trotted to the ranch, Old Mary—for all her discomforts—riding as well as any, for she had been in the saddle from childhood.

The Woman had plenty of beans and bannock, and there was hot, sweet tea and dry salty pork.

Old Atchikoos admired the walls of the big new house, while Mary and the Woman clucked over the baby.

Mary said: "Fall-time you' man killum bear. Make plenty grease. You rubbum good, you' li'l papoose."

Then down the trail they clattered, to be seen no more for weeks. Mary did not get her shawl that time.

Hardly had Atchikoos and his squaw disappeared down the

pack-trail when the Kid called from behind the cabin. They all turned, looking in the direction of his pointed finger.

Coming very slowly, on stiff legs, old Starlight was picking his way down the steep and grassy slope of Moose Ridge.

The Man could hardly believe his eyes. He gave a low whistle, and Starlight, who with hanging head was making for the corral, paused and uttered a dry whinny in reply. Deliberately he turned towards the little party and stood, shifting tired legs. His eyes were sunken, and his rib-shadows deep. His erstwhile glossy coat was encrusted with sweat, which had dried in dirty white flakes down his legs.

"Well, Starlight, I thought you'd come!" said the Kid, and ran a hand over the peaked rump of his favourite.

"Turn him in the corral and feed him some hay," was all the Man could trust himself to say.

The Woman stroked the old horse's nose, talking softly. But there was that in both their eyes which spoke more eloquently than simple words.

Old Starlight, pensioned from hard work, only ridden occasionally by the Kid, was a Steel Dust horse—the finest breeding in the West. He had been a gift from a rancher "down a-ways" who had said: "You folks can use another pony. Give him a good home. The old fellow can teach the Kid a lot. But watch his kidneys—they trouble him."

Old Starlight, a good roping horse; why, even the Man was proud to ride him a short way.

There came another whinny from the hillside. It was Julie, the bay mare, this time. They could just see her against the blue sky at the hilltop, with Ted, the crop-eared buckskin crowding behind her. Starlight answered Julie's enquiry, and the two started down carefully and slowly. Soon all three were in the corral, all three tired, scratched, and sweat-streaked. That they had come from far to the east was evident from the ochre mud of Yellow Creek and the white clay of Thunder Crossing which still clung to fetlocks and hocks.

But where was Julie's yearling, the most prized of all, that would grow up to be a golden-coated, silver-maned palamino? They looked from one to the other; shook their heads. None voiced the obvious. To the horse traders, the yearling—unbranded as yet—meant real cash money. Once it had been gentle-broke, any tycoon in Calgary would pay . . .

"Not taking any more chances for a bit," the Man said. "Turn them in the pasture when they've rested. They aren't safe on the range; and that way, if the little 'un comes back, he'll find them. There's grass enough for now. If we turn 'em on the range—they'll maybe go a-ways, and the little 'un may find them some place where those fellows will pick him up again."

Several days went by, and there were no signs of the palamino. One night the Man, musing aloud, said: "Guess I'll have to turn out those horses after all. Grass is getting short this dry weather, and we'll have to bring in the work stock soon for haying."

And next morning he remarked: "Don't see those horses around. Guess I'll look 'em over."

The Kid looked uncomfortable at this. "Well, Dad," he said finally, "I guess I turned them out when I went to feed the team—I thought that's what you wanted."

The Man tried to control himself, but his nerves were frazzled from the work, the planning, and the recent events.

"Dammit, man!" he roared. "What the devil do you want to *think* for. Why'n hell don't you ask? You finish your breakfast, saddle Robin—he's in, isn't he?—and go bring Starlight and Julie back."

The Woman said: "I think he did his best, dear," but the Man couldn't reply.

Small looked sober at her father's words, and the Man went out, thinking: "Maybe I've done wrong. This nip-and-tuck life! —don't know whether you're wasting your time or not. Maybe it's not fair to the folks. That Kid does well with his correspondence course, but it might be better for him to go to school."

Noon came, and the Kid had not returned. The Man was worried. The youngster was sensitive, shy, not given to talk. Not the rancher type, either.

He saddled Fox and followed the Kid's tracks far enough to get the general direction. Near the mouth of a coulee he saw something move. A horse. It was Robin, grazing. With his heart in his mouth, the Man galloped up. Surely the Kid hadn't been thrown? By Robin, of all horses?

But no. There he was, on his knees. He raised his head. "Hi, Dad," he said quietly. "Worrying about me? Sorry."

And then the Man saw that the Kid had just finished skinning a middle-sized cinnamon bear—a two-year-old, he judged, and the palest he'd ever seen, almost like a polar bear!

"How in hell did you find that thing?" he said, his anger rising again. He'd wanted to finish that bit of breaking today, instead of running around the country . . .

"Shot it," said the Kid.

The Man glanced at the Kid's saddle, saw the .22 rifle hanging from the horn. "With *that* thing?" he asked.

"Yep," said the Kid, rising. "It's sure lucky I had that skinning knife I sent to Eatons for—though it *is* a bit dull."

"O.K.," snapped the Man. Then, with a grin: "Well done! But don't ever tackle a bear with a .22 again. It's not safe. A wounded bear can make mince-meat of a man."

"Oh, sure," was the reply. "But I had a 'long-rifle' shell and shot from Robin's back. Then I galloped away like he—the dickens, in case he'd chase me. But he didn't. He was dead as a doornail."

Together they mounted, the Kid leaving the blood to turn brown on his knife. Behind his saddle flapped the bear hide. The Kid was going to give it to Atchikoos' squaw and ask her to make a pair of winter mitts. Behind the man's saddle hung a fat bear ham to be dry-salted and smoked.

Starlight, Julie, and the buckskin were feeding close by and were driven home to be confined again.

It was the next morning that they found the golden colt, dead and already bloated up. He lay against the pasture fence, on the outside. He had staggered that far, and one glance was enough to show the Man why he had lagged behind.

He had been castrated, recently, and without benefit of disinfectant. Flies were massed on the stinking wound. It made the Man sick to think of those tortured miles—the stiff, short steps, the long rests in the deep willows out of sight, nursing his pain; the effort of starting off again, stumbling among the the deadfall, puffing up the steep slopes, crossing the creeks, longing to die, but driven on by his instinct to find the bunch.

Reconstructing the thing, the Man concluded that the bunch

had been held in some remote brush corral while the operation had been performed. Somehow, hungry and thirsty, led by Starlight, they had escaped, and the old horse had wasted no time. The pace must have opened the colt's wound, for no doubt the perpetrators of the deed had chased them and tried to recapture them. Starlight had outrun the pursuers, and they must have passed the colt as he slipped aside from the bunch into some shady, cooler fastness. The riders would certainly have turned back, cursing, before letting themselves be sighted on the ridge; and the Man now cursed them—hide, hooves, and hair—whoever they were.

And the colt, by-passed, had resumed his trail of pain, following doggedly where the bunch had gone. He had made it, stout of heart, only to die where every horse wants to die—where he was foaled.

Twice that summer the Man saw the Black Wolf. Once broadside on, as he rounded a sharp turn of the creek. An easy shot, and he reached for his rifle, only to touch the empty scabbard. He had lent his Winchester to the Boy only that morning. He swore softly, and when he raised his eyes the wolf was gone.

Later, the Man and the Woman, while riding one evening around Wild Horse Point, found a half-eaten calf. It was the second such loss that year: And hardly had they left the scene than they saw the killer himself, standing still as death and as black as night. He was near the edge of a patch of ground-birch, from which he stared at them with bleak, uninviting eyes. The Woman turned to her companion. "Why," she said, "I had no idea timber wolves were so big, or had such long legs! It looks like a yearling steer—and why," she added, "do you always see him when you don't have a rifle?" Those few words broke the spell, and when they looked again the bush stood as empty as if no wolf had ever stood there.

"Confound it," thought the Man. "Left my rifle behind again." He spoke slowly. "I can hardly believe it myself, but they say a wolf can smell metal, and all old hunters tell me if you want to see one, don't take a rifle."

Whether that explained it or not, the Man had no luck with traps either. He set them on the game-trails which the wolves followed and in circles around their lying-up places, but with only one catch, and that was a pup in the fall. Although he boiled the traps in willow-bark and used only clean gloves to handle them; although he buried them, covering the jaws with paper-thin birch-bark with dry dirt sifted over the top; although he then backed up and smoothed out all tracks with an eagle's wing—the results, except for that once, were always the same.

The traps would be carefully stepped around, or sometimes even flipped over and sprung by a quick jab of a paw from underneath, and in final derision, urinated on.

In the meantime their nineteen calves had been reduced to fifteen by the time Atchikoos found the den. After that the killing stopped, for a while anyway.

The Man wondered where the wolves had moved to. Far away, he hoped. But money was scarce, and the bounty for the one in the fall helped. He felt sure it was just a passing wolf, for it seemed to be alone.

Chapter 8

The crop was tall now, and heading out; already the young grass was showing up among the oat stalks. The Man planned to cut the oats with a horse-mower and make it into hay. To get a mower up the narrow pack-trail would be impossible; they would have to make at least a rough wagon-road. This country was not like the prairies, where he'd lived as a young man: not like the prairies where you could drive a wagon almost anywhere, and after a couple of trips you had a plain trail in the grass.

It was decided that the whole family would go. They couldn't leave the Woman alone, and anyway the days would be long and the work hard, and it would be fine to have a cook. The Woman herself was thrilled. She'd much rather ride and camp and cook than stick by herself at Deep Springs.

They would take three teams, one dragging the plough and the others carrying harness and packs with grub, bedding, axes, and the tent. The Woman would ride Robin, with Small in her arms. The pace would be slow and easy.

They planned to work their way down to the junction of the pack-trail and the east-west wagon-road which followed the river, thirty miles away. Here they would find the wagons the Man had left there early in the spring, as well as the "democrat" buggy, mower, and hay rake.

They started off early, but it took most of the day to widen the trail through the bush below Moose Ridge and past the buttes into Thunder Creek valley. The Man sent the Boy scouting ahead from time to time, changing the trail in places to take advantage of every possible patch of open prairie. With so much stopping to lop back willows, to cut standing trees and saw through deadfall blocking the way, the Woman was able to dismount for up to an hour at a time. While Small slept she looked at the lovely wild flowers or picked ripe strawberries. The raspberries and saskatoons were beginning to ripen too, so she filled a lard pail with a mixed lot, which would go down well at dinner. A great hawk wheeled overhead, screaming loudly above the axe strokes. She looked up, admiring the bird, and recognizing it as a red-tailed buzzard, a harmless killer of squirrels and rabbits. The Man knew birds and had pointed out these hawks before. Then she saw the nest, a great bulky mass of sticks all of fifty feet up, in a stout poplar by the trail; the axemen had steered around that tree.

At dusk they set up the tent at Thunder Creek.

Next morning the Boy hitched the team on to the plough, and with the Man at the handles they ploughed a few furrows down both banks of the deep ravine, taking the team to the top after each furrow and dragging the plough up on its side, for they could not work uphill.

The Man had previously made a heavy "drag," from two-inch planks and four by fours. This was like a simple snowplough, built in the form of a triangle. Rocks would be piled in the centre to give it weight, and pulled by a team at the right angle, it would serve to turn the ploughed-up loose dirt out and downhill, thus making a level trail on the side of a slope.

Another full day was spent here, and two more cutting brush and trees and ploughing down into the main valley of the Cutbank. The valley had to be traversed for seven miles, and the winding creek crossed three times. Several boggy spots had to be corduroyed with short lengths of poles, cut from the neighbouring bush.

Nevertheless, the fourth evening found them at the foot of the last hill, above which a couple operated a stopping house on the settlement road. From here it was another thirty miles to the jumble of buildings which comprized the village at which they got their mail and supplies. A rough wagon-road already wound up this hill, for the stopping-house man hauled his water from the creek, so now there was at least a rough and narrow road all the way from Deep Springs, and the Man would now be able to use his wagons. It was at this stopping house that the two wagons and the machinery awaited them.

The Woman enjoyed a visit with the stout and breathless lady who really ran the stopping house, while the men greased the wagons and made everything ship-shape. People who have been isolated for many weeks enjoy talking, and the party stayed all that day and the next night. The Woman made out an order for a number of household goods, including her curtain material, and the good lady of the house promised to send it in by the first passer-by.

The son of the house had recently returned from war service, and entertained the boys with racy descriptions of his adventures, while the Man talked with their host of the sage-brush country of the south, which they both had known. Meanwhile the host's wife and the Woman admired and played with Small, with many a "Land's sakes!" and "I declare!" from the breathless one.

The return journey was arranged like this. One team was put to the democrat—a spring-wagon, something like a buggy, with its narrow wheels, but much more solidly built and longer in the box than an ordinary buggy. It was actually built for two seats, one behind the other. With the hind seat removed, it could carry a load of nearly half a ton. In this wagon the Woman, with Small on her lap, made herself comfortable, while the Kid handled the fast-stepping team.

Next came the Man with a wagon loaded with a set of separated disk-harrows, four sections of toothed harrows, and on the top, the plank drag. It was pulled by a steady old team. Behind him came the Boy with the biggest team, Pete and Nancy, drawing a heavier wagon carrying the mower, with its tongue removed, and the dismantled hay rake, with its teeth tied in a big bundle. Both loads were held solid by tight log-chains. The buggy, of course, carried groceries, blankets, and the grub box, with the tent folded over all and roped down solidly.

The trail was dry and dusty. Only a heavy rain could delay their return, but that event would be accepted philosophically by people who knew you could not hurry things on the frontier. If that happened, you simply made camp and waited for the creeks to go down and the swamp-holes to dry.

This road would be strictly a good-weather road, useless in spring when the frost was coming out. No car would be able to follow it, which suited them well. Car-roads brought hunters, crooked developers, and all sorts of folk.

By noon they had arrived at the foot of the hill where they were to climb out of the valley, which now narrowed to a jumble of cliffs and cutbanks. The muddy fords were behind them, and the prospect of leaving the depths and the hot bush for the cool breeze on top was a welcome one.

Camp was made and lunch eaten. All that afternoon the Man and the Boy worked at levelling the hill-trail. They took turns at driving the heavy drag or at plying the crowbar and the shovel, loosening rocks, digging out the bank, or tidying up as the dirt, sod, and stones were pushed to the lower side.

The Kid slept in the shade. He was tired.

The Woman baked a bannock, put some dried meat to stew, and then set to picking strawberries for supper. The fruit hung so thickly among the grass that she noticed that the wagon tires were red with the juice. The mosquitoes were bad, a sign of thunder in the air. She threw a net of cheesecloth over the sleeping Small, then dabbed insect repellent—"dope" they called it—over her own face and neck. She made this at home. Citronella and pyrethrum were some of the ingredients. Her menfolk scorned it. Her brother in Kenya grew pyrethrums on his farm. How things made your mind jump about! She thought she'd rather have wolves and zero weather than snakes and heat. The men heard her singing as they came down the trail, their clothes heavy with dust.

Next morning they got the wagons to the top, one at a time, using four horses on each. The buggy followed, and by mid-morning they arrived at the top of Thunder Creek coulee. It was five in the evening when the men finished the near side of the hill. They returned to the top and had supper while the horses rested and munched their oats.

Now the Man mounted the seat. The hill before them was steep, and it was sideling too. It would take a good team to hold back such a load by its pole, for its weight might put the horses down. And it would take good driving to keep the hind wheels from skidding sideways at the curves and dragging the whole outfit down the bank to the creek three hundred feet below. It was with this possibility in mind that he had seen to it that each wagon was equipped with a length of log-chain fastened to the hind axle. In this way the teams could be "doubled up." The Boy, familiar with the job, now brought up Pete and Nancy with their neck yoke buckled on. He threaded the several feet of loose chain through the neck-yoke ring and grabbed it back to itself by its hook—a hitch easy to undo in an emergency.

The Boy, on foot, picked up his lines, backed his team to take up the slack chain. "O.K.!" he shouted.

The Man nodded and clucked to his horses. Slowly the wagon began to roll, digging into the soft, newly turned earth. The men held their lines, not too tight, but ready to hold the teams at the worst places. At the steepest part—and it *was* steep—the teams settled into their breechings with a grunt.

"Steady!" called the Man. If the wagon rolled too fast, his horses would be pushed off their feet. Momentarily he wished he had put on the steel shoe under one hind wheel. But that could get you into trouble too. A shoe tended to drag you either into the bank or over the edge. So did a rough-lock. They crabbed a wagon, and there wasn't an inch to spare; and besides, either of those devices rutted a soft road and spoilt it.

So the Man, lines taut, carefully guiding his team, and the Boy, a skilled teamster, holding back the wagon from the rear, inched their way down. The Boy kept his horses well towards the bank, so that the rear wheel could not slip over the edge. Lucky the road was dry.

They unhitched at the bottom and toiled to the top for the second wagon, the horses coughing in the dust.

The buggy came last. The Man drove, holding the brake handle down with his right foot. The little horses braced their feet cleverly, never letting the democrat get the advantage, while the good ash pole groaned. The Woman looked straight ahead after one quick glance below, where she could see the treetops bending in the breeze.

The tent was set up at the bottom.

Next morning the levelling began up the opposite slope. This was steeper, though shorter, and required the laborious digging out of a number of stumps which the plough had skidded around. Noon came and the job was not finished, so after a lunch the men tackled it again, and it was not till after supper that they were ready to take the wagons up. The Man wanted to get them at least to the top, for thunder rumbled far to the north. The horses were doubled up, Pete and Nancy this time on the lead.

The Boy took the lines. He liked driving four-up. The Man followed on foot, ready to block a hind wheel should there be trouble.

"Hup! Hup, there!" shouted the Boy, standing on the creaking, swaying load, the line-ends doubled in his right hand.

The horses hit the foot of the hill on the trot and began to scramble up, straining and puffing. Twice one of the leaders almost went down, but he recovered during the tense second that the other three held. If they couldn't make it with four horses they had only two alternatives. One was to go to the ranch for a third team; the other was to lighten the load, and where on that narrow sideling track could they put the stuff? The Boy was looking desperately for a place halfway up the slope where he could rest the horses. Nancy was almost done. She hesitated, the Boy roared again, just as he saw a short, almost level spot twenty yards ahead. Would he make it? The wagon creaked, the horses scrambled, and the leaders reached the level, and good footing. A few more steps and the whole outfit was safe. The driver shouted, "Whoa."

The Man chucked a rock behind a wheel. The horses were blowing, their nostrils red and as large as teacups. Spume flecked their necks, sweat ran from their bellies and fell in drops, pitting the dust. Their flanks heaved, and the muscles of their shoulders fluttered like leaves.

The Boy knew better than to rest them too long. That way, they would lose their fire. "Keep their blood up," the Man had always said. "When they want to go, don't hold them back. It discourages them."

The Boy saw the heaving flanks steadying down, the tremor of the shoulders subside. One of the leaders tossed his head and lifted a hairy hoof.

"Hup!" bellowed the Boy, and snapped the lines.

Scrambling, half-falling, the horses dug in their hooves, pulling until their shoulder muscles bulged and until their breathing became a sustained roar: Then suddenly they were at the top, on the level.

This was the heaviest load. The second wagon went up after the horses had a half hour's rest.

It was nearly dark when the teams came down again to be watered, given some oats, and turned loose in the goose-grass to graze. The buggy still sat at the bottom. It would have to carry up the womenfolk, the tent, and the gear. They all turned in.

The campfire burned down to white ashes. The horses blundered about, thumping and breaking twigs, and amid these familiar sounds and the snores of the men the Woman and Small slept dreamlessly on their spruce-bed. Her last thought had been: "Over a week to go and come thirty miles! I wonder if the electric trains still run from London to Hampton Wick at sixty miles an hour? Or was that a dream . . . ?"

Next morning was very still. The sprucetops were silent. By the time breakfast had been eaten and the horses caught up, it was sweltering and oppressive.

"You boys take the teams up and hitch on the wagons," the Man directed. "Take my old team, Kid, and follow behind. You'll manage them. I'll bring up the buggy, and if we don't catch up at Moose Point, wait. The road's pretty sideling through the bush, and you may get hung up on a stump."

The boys gulped the last of the coffee and started up the hill, each riding a horse, the heavy heel-chains jingling.

Quickly, deftly, the Man packed the gear, roped down the load, and hitched up the ponies. The Woman had washed at the creek and was now doing her hair, plaiting it in two long braids like an Indian. He scuffed out the campfire, pouring on water, put the pail under the seat, and mounted.

"Ready?" he called. She picked up Small, handed her up, grabbed the dashboard, and was beside him.

"We'd best hurry," the Man said. "See that thunderhead hanging over the buttes? If we get a downpour before we reach the top—well, we won't reach it. Once you take the duff and sod off this clay, a rain will make it slick as a greased plank."

The democrat began to creak its way upward. It had been a Provincial Police vehicle till that force had been motorized. The Man had been lucky to get it at a surplus sale. It was almost the last one in the country.

Suddenly the sun was obscured. There came a peal of thunder, bouncing and rolling down the valley, and before it died away, another. The wind blew suddenly cold. The trees swayed. They heard one fall with a crash behind them. The Man glanced quickly under the seat. Yes, the axe and the cross-cut saw were there. He might need them.

The rain came, as the wind suddenly dropped, while they were still almost a quarter mile from the summit. It came, not lashing, not in drops, but in a steady pour, gushing down so that they could feel its weight, muting the thunder, blotting out the valley. In seconds the dirt-trail became a sea of mud.

"*Git* up there!" The Man swung the lines and brought them down with a crack on the two wet, straining rumps.

Before they had made ten yards, both ponies were on their knees, sliding backwards in the grease, unable to get a footing with the full weight of the buggy on their traces. The front wheels were cramping against the body of the buggy, as the hind wheels slid sideways.

"Get out," the Man said. "Throw Small on the bank—the high side."

The Woman managed to throw the baby up in the grass and scrub, and somehow scrambled up herself. She saw the Man jump to the ground, saw his feet slip behind him, saw him crawl on hands and knees, desperately wrenching at the draw-pin to release the eveners and free the horses.

The off-horse had rolled on its side, groaning. The harness was taut as a fiddle-string.

The other, still on his knees, might soon go down.

The whole outfit, horses and buggy, was slipping slowly towards the edge, in spite of the brake.

Momentarily, a wheel held against a rock, and with the slack the bolt came loose. The pole left the neck-yoke ring and swung to one side, releasing the cramped wheel. The buggy rolled again, slid over the edge without a sound, and turned upside down against a poplar tree ten feet below, its wheels slowly revolving in the air.

Now for the horses. Quickly the Man unsnapped the cross-checks, undid the breast-snaps from the neck yoke, and they were no longer a team, but separated horses. Heaving on the tail of the off-pony, which could not regain his feet for all his struggles, he managed to slide it over the bank. It landed unharmed in a patch of willows, got to its feet, and began to tear unconcernedly at the timber-grass. The other, released from the pull of the buggy, rose gingerly from its knees and stood trembling, its toes dug into the greasy trail. Water and mud streamed from it.

The rain was over. The sun shone as hot as before, and a hermit thrush sent its rich chimes ringing from the dripping spruce below.

The Man joined the Woman on the bank above. "Give me Small," he said. The little one, splashed and scratched, was whimpering. "Come on!" he said.

The Woman, bedraggled, her splashed face glowing, her chestnut braids like rats' tails, followed. They trudged to level ground, pulling themselves up by saplings, and sat on a fallen log to dry themselves. The Woman stripped Small, letting the hot sun warm her while her clothes dried. The mosquitoes were bad at that season, and she kept them off as well as she could with a leafy twig.

The Man left her there. The near horse still stood, afraid to move, but breathing easily. The trail would soon be dry under that sun, and in the meantime the horse down the bank had good footing in the grass and low willows. The Man clambered down the bank, jumped on the pony, and with harness flying, scrambled up in pursuit of the teams. He caught up with the boys at the buttes. Although on the level, their heavy loads had started to slide around on the gumbo, and they had stopped and taken shelter under the wagons. The Boy unhitched his team, tied a log-chain to their eveners, and followed him back.

The trail was drying to sticky mud and was no longer so slick and greasy.

The other pony had climbed to the top, where the Woman caught and tied it up. The buggy was righted by the Boy fastening his chain to the downhill side and then stepping up his team while the Man assisted by holding all steady. Then the big team took it to the top. The well-roped load had not shifted. Not even a tin cup was dented.

By nightfall the whole caravan pulled into Deep Springs, and by next morning the troubles were forgotten—as such things are by people who have to face a new day and catch up on work. All that mattered was that the wagons and machinery were home safely, and that neither man nor beast was hurt.

The Woman's mosquito bites itched for days, of course, and the baby's sunburn had to be touched up with the Woman's one luxury, Nivea cream.

So the old pack-trail, first blazed in 1898 by Inspector Moody and his Northwest Police boys as an overland route to the Yukon, became a wagon-road, of sorts. As far as Deep Springs, anyway. In bad weather pack-horses would still be the best transportation. Even in winter a chinook could turn the snow to slippery ice. Once, later, the Man had to abandon his sleigh halfway up Thunder Creek valley for that reason, and return with pack-horses for the Christmas mail and treats. So it was on the trail—hardly a trip without trouble for a vehicle—while pack-horses, running loose, could choose individual routes by taking the side and getting footing among the twigs and spruce needles.

No wonder the Man didn't go "out" often; there was just no use worrying about mail.

Anyway the oats were cut, raked, and stacked, and there would be no shortage of feed for the stock, come winter.

In late September the Man and the Boy tackled the trail again with two wagons. They had to bring up lumber for the floors and the roof of the new house, and windows to fill the gaps cut in the walls.

It was getting dark and starting to rain when, only four miles from home, they got halfway through the bush on the sideling trail below Moose Ridge. The Man was on the lead wagon, the Boy close behind. It took good driving to avoid the fresh-cut stumps on either side, and the teamsters peered from their high loads, trying to see them.

The Man heard the Boy say: "Whoa-a!"

Both teams stopped. Looking back, the Man could see little in the gloom except the dim outline of Pete, the Boy's off-horse. Pete was a grey, almost white. He heard the Boy get down.

"What's up?" the Man called.

"Wagon slid. There's a stump against the axle. I'll try the axe."

The Man heard a couple of blows. One obviously hit the wagon tire. Not too good for the axe. The Boy had no room to work, except in short, chopping strokes. He only knew where the stump was by feeling for it. They were both so damned tired too. And hungry. The Man's team threw up their heads, making the heel-chains ring. And the Man heard another sound, from right above his head where a big balsam-poplar spread its branches. A low, fierce sound, something between hissing and hoarse breathing. He knew what it was. A bear.

And she was angry. Probably had cubs. She'd sent them up the tree at the chucking, groaning approach of the wagons.

The Man spoke quietly to his horses, lines tight against a possible runaway.

He spoke again, keeping his voice calm: "How're you getting on?"

"Can't get at it!" the Boy shouted back.

"Well, leave it," the Man said. "There's a bear in the tree above me. Sounds like she's coming down! Can't hold the horses much longer. Hurry and unhitch. Work your horses around the *right* side of my wagon. The bear's in a tree on the *left.*"

With that the Man jumped down. He wasted no time with the heel-chains, but pulled the draw-bolt. The horses jumped forward. The pole fell with a thud, the eveners rattling on their heels. The Boy was doing the same. Both teams took off up the trail, the men hanging grimly to the lines, their feet dragging.

Behind them they heard the bear land with a thud on the lumber.

After a quarter mile the teams slowed to a walk and stopped. Each man jumped on his near horse, and they trotted home through the wet, black night.

When they returned in daylight they found only the bear's

tracks on the soft ground. They chained the near wagon backward, turned the wheel clear of the stump, and were home by noon.

By dark they had the downstairs floor laid and nailed to the squared spruce joists.

By the time snow came the house was finished, the walls plastered with clay and all snug. From now on the little cabin would be used as a bunkhouse for extra help or visitors. But blankets, food, and wood for its stove were kept replenished.

In case of fire, the Man did not want people freezing their feet in the snow—and perhaps losing them—for want of shelter. They could always keep alive, hugger-mugger, in the cabin. This was part of survival; to foresee every emergency, like the possibility of fire in a place where there was no neighbour within walking distance.

Even the Woman began to think that this self-dependent existence might be really safer than relying on the services of others. You always knew the exact situation. You couldn't be inconvenienced by a strike, by a plumber who couldn't come just then, by a telephone line that was down, an office which closed on Saturday, a store that shut at six o'clock, or a train that went by a new timetable. Here you did things as they came along, or according to the weather.

Those stacks of feed were needed. The winter was a bad one. The chinook didn't blow from November to March, and the snow was almost too deep for a saddle-horse, while between the storms the thermometer dropped to minus thirty, to minus forty, for three cold nights, to minus sixty.

But the cattle, bedded in a spruce bluff and fed every day with a load of green oat hay, carried their flesh till spring.

Chapter 9

A March chinook came at last. A great arch of scudding clouds hung over the mountains, the wind blew in the treetops until the tall spruces by the barn creaked and bent their heads, and the snow began to settle.

By the end of the month the creek was running, and its steady roar could be heard above the wind. The cattle began to leave the feed forked out to them; they sniffed the breeze, lowing at the scent of earth-smells after the still frostiness of the past months. An old blue cow plunged through the drifts to an open shoulder of the hillside above. Others followed, until a packed trail showed their passage.

The jingle of the Man's sleigh-bells rang out, carried on the wind, but the blue cow, tearing the exposed grass, only raised her head momentarily at the sound. One yearling, used to the rush which that sound had provoked throughout the winter, started back through the drift, bawling. But looking back and seeing no followers, she rejoined the now-scattered herd as they grazed slowly uphill. She was one of twenty yearling heifers the Man had bought last fall to make use of the heavy oat crop. They would calve next year.

Some of the cattle, having reached the top of the first bench, were now plunging brisket-deep through the drifts which still hung on the banks of the shallow coulees, pausing to nip at the red rose berries before clambering up to a new shoulder where the grass showed tawny and inviting. To the Man below they looked like ants moving about.

The Man forked off the rest of the load, driving in a circle around the opening among the protective spruce.

"Damn you!" he shouted, half-angered, half-pleased. "It's here if you want it!"

The sound of bells died away as the team trotted the half mile home.

The Black Wolf nudged his mate. All day he had lain on the bare clay of his lookout above the canyon, alternately sleeping or staring with unwinking eyes over the sweep of the valley and hills to the north. Two miles away, Moose Point, now bare of snow, loomed solidly above the scrublands. Now at dusk he saw some tiny dots work their way up from the willow swamps of Burnt Creek. They came in single file, plodding with heads down, gradually scattering over the point. The wolf knew they were wild horses and knew they were grazing on the open grass—a relief from the everlasting winter job of pawing through deep and crusted snow.

The horses had wintered along Burnt Creek, sheltered from the bitter winds, digging out the marsh grass which still showed some green under the snow.

The Black Wolf nudged his wife again, and she in turn looked towards the almost-grown pups—the second litter since Atchikoos had disturbed them at Wolf Point. The pups rose, sensing that here was hunting. Perhaps this would be the last lesson from the old ones, for they were already getting restless, on the point of leaving to find mates and dens of their own. Following the three-footed bitch, they slipped down the canyon bottom and crossed Cutbank Creek.

The Black Wolf was already on his way. He could accomplish his plans only by making a wide circle. The horses would be thrown off their guard by their eagerness to fill up without effort. The foals, almost colts now, would be in fair shape and juicy; nor would all be weaned, for mares are good-natured, often allowing a colt to suck for two seasons. The mares would be thin and weak from making milk all winter, and now would be heavy with another burden. Their hooves would be long and clumsy from treading soft snow all winter; it would take several weeks on the high ridges to break off the excess hoof-horn and harden their feet.

And best of all for the wolf's plans, it was starting to freeze now, as the sun and wind went down. The bare ground would be slippery, the slope steep, and the horses were not likely to move but to gather at the foot of the point to sleep till just after midnight, standing hip-shot and low-headed. If they were surprised they would make heavy going of it on the slick ground.

The Black Wolf followed the water-worn gully of Burnt Creek for a mile and a half at a steady lope. He came to the area where the horses had spent the last few weeks. The snow was pawed up in ridges, and on the south side of the willow clumps he could tell they had slept and sunned themselves, for the ground was strewn thick with dung. He turned west and followed the tracks up the ridge till they turned to wind their way below the summit to reach the point. He left the tracks without a pause, reached the top, and then turned south to the big rock which lay on the brow of the point. Here he sank low in the trench which bordered the rock; a trench once dug by the hooves of wood buffalo as they scratched and rubbed themselves, giving the big stone itself a worn, smooth surface.

The wolf heard hooves moving a hundred feet below, crunching on the now-frozen ground; heard a colt smacking its lips as it sucked its dam; heard a horse sigh, and another shift from one hind foot to the other.

There were seven mares, all but one with colts from last year, three following two-year-olds, and the stallion. The wolf did not know that the horse traders had roped out the other two-year-olds, although he had found one lying dead. Its neck had been broken against a rope tied fast to the fork of a rider's saddle as it tried to jump a dry-wash. The wolves had gained handsomely from this mishap.

The wolf listened. The others should be in place now. He tensed. A roaring wolf howl shattered the stillness from below. He heard the horses snort and jump. Raising himself he answered howl with howl, the fiendish noise reverberating from point to creek to bush to point, so that it would have taken a smart man—or horse—to know from which direction it came.

The horses, following their instinct to seek high ground, started uphill, slipping, sliding, while the stallion grunted and neighed, biting at their rumps with his wicked yellow teeth. But the Black Wolf met them, loping back and forth across the brown of the hill, his stinking breath terrifying the already-frightened animals. Colts whickered hysterically as more howls came from below, triumphant now. The wolves down there had a two-year-old surrounded. The dry mare dodged cleverly to one side around the shoulder of the point, calling for followers. The stallion was working to the limit of his strength, slipping, fighting for footing. He crashed into a mare, knocking her colt over. The colt squealed, threshing its legs, and started to slide down the slope. The Black Wolf, with one bound from the top, was at its throat in a second. Its dam whimpered with concern and essayed to turn back, but the stallion raked her ribs and drove her to where the dry mare, her tail high, ran in circles to attract the attention of the rest, who had fled in every direction. Yet, instinctively seeking the haven of high ground, they worked to either side of the ridge and now galloped, whickering, to the top. The stallion answered and joined them. On sighting the dry mare the whole band thundered towards her. She at once started north along the ridgetop at a swinging pace. They all fell in behind. They were saved. The lost are soon forgotten.

The two-year-old, meanwhile, finding himself surrounded, backed his rump to a clay bank and stood at bay with lowered head, one forefoot raised to crush any wolf that tried to seize him by the nose. The wolves were silent now, ready for the final grim act. The only sounds were the padding of their feet and the horse's explosive snorts.

One of the wolves feinted at the two-year-old's throat and sprang back. The horse followed, rearing and ready to strike. Another young wolf made a bound and tore a pound of flesh from the two-year-old's rump, swallowing the bloody morsel as it jumped aside. The horse, with a scream, turned on his new tormentor.

The wolves could hear their black father tearing at the colt as it still struggled. Each to his kill. They renewed their efforts. As the horse spun around, it was another wolf's turn to tear off

a larger chunk from the edge of the dripping wound, easily evading the feeble kick from that tortured leg.

Death came to the young horse slowly. Turn which way he might, there was always the red-hot pain of flesh torn from flanks, from ribs, from buttocks, till, covered with blood and spume, he sank slowly down, first to his knees, then prone. The young wolves crouched to their feast, but it was not until they had torn open his belly and dragged out his liver that the two-year-old laid his head down, his eyes glazing over.

The bitch had taken no active part. Her job was to lead, to show the way. The young wolves had to learn, and in any case her crippled foot was against her in a rough-and-tumble. She now fed with her mate, burrowing deep into the colt.

The stars were fading when, their bellies bulging, the wolves returned to the canyon. They would not move for at least two days.

Flying over Moose Point, a quartering raven saw, in the pale primrose dawn, a smirch on the hillside below. The bird circled lower, until it knew this was blood, mixed with broken grass and sage twigs, surrounding two dark, untidy objects. He croaked, circled still lower on easy wings, and came to rest on the horse's head.

There were soon empty sockets where those glazed eyes had been.

His croak was heard, and as if from nowhere two more of his dark kind appeared, together with a long-tailed magpie.

Towards dusk a coyote came on to a wolf-track, crossing a patch of snow. The prairie wolf shrank back, looked to right and left. But there was blood in the track. It smelt good. Nose to the ground, he, too, arrived at the carcasses and crept between the ribs of the largest, from where the inward parts had been torn.

Chapter 10

The Man had not passed by Moose Point all winter, and it was well into April before he had any need to go that way.

It was calving time. This meant a lot of riding, and on this fine spring day the world looked good as he began to ride among the scattered cattle. Two calves this morning. Up and sucking. Good! No trouble there.

He rode on. Over half of the cattle must have moved, though, and he made a wide circle till he struck their tracks angling up the ridge. They had turned south, towards Moose Point. That was the best spot for early grass; that, and eastward along the south slope, across Burnt Creek and towards the buttes. They could not get there before because of the deep drifts, but those had almost melted away. The cattle couldn't be far ahead, for there was fresh dung along the trail.

Then he heard a bellow ahead of him, and another—not the high, angry bellow which tells of an attack; rather the mumbling, grumbling sounds announcing something strange.

He came to the big rock at a trot, edged over the brink, and saw, below him, the cattle milling around, crowding about something. Some had their tongues out and pawed the ground. Hell! He hoped it wasn't a dead cow or calf.

Fox slid to the bottom, scattering the animals. The Man saw the remains of a colt and another horse. White pelvis bones.

Skulls dragged aside by coyotes, bits of dried skin still clinging to the frontal bones. The bigger one had been a blazed-face sorrel. Piles of tail-hair, racks of ribs whitewashed by ravens. And hardly any odour in that keen, dry air. No tracks; they had been washed away. But he knew at once it was wolf work.

He hadn't heard a howl or seen a track all winter—but then, the snow had been deep and there'd been no real need to ride far.

The cattle were making a circle again, pawing dirt and bellowing in those tones which told the world and each other that death was abroad. Hurriedly, he counted them. Twelve cows and ten yearlings. That was about right, but he'd look around a bit more.

He turned towards Burnt Creek. No tracks through the willows, but he'd look at the crossing to make sure. Cattle had to leave tracks, thank goodness, or you would never be able to find them in this jumble of small prairies, poplar thickets, spruce, and deadfall so cut up with coulees, creeks, and sidehills. On the prairies, he remembered, you could ride to the top of a knoll and see cattle a long way, but here you went by tracks! And still he wouldn't trade this ranch for a south-country one. It wasn't easy, even for wolves, here—too many different ways to go unseen, too much dead ground. You couldn't look below every cutbank, and if it wasn't for tracks you would have to ride every inch of the ground. Tracks; dung; the smell of cattle; that was it. And a good horse, who knew how to swing his head, prick his ears. . . . Maybe you needed more feed here, but at least you had enough rain to *grow* it. It only took work . . .

Thus musing, as every rider does when he is alone, he arrived at the crossing. There were no cattle-tracks, but he checked Fox to stare hard at a wolf-track in some dried mud. Probably a week old, he surmised. Coming back he looked up at the long range of hills. The slopes looked inviting, washed with the almost blue-green of the bunch grass. He could smell it. And the budding sage.

The Man liked this part of the range. The slopes were treeless, all grooved in parallel lines by grazing animals—buffalo originally, he supposed, but now traversed by cattle and horses as they grazed the steep sides. This was like a bit of the southern Alberta of his youth, the Chin coulee country. Even the early crocuses and yellow buffalo beans were the same, and the sage. This bunch of cattle, anyway, could stay here all summer. There was Burnt Creek, and if that narrow gully went dry there were good springs below the buttes to the east.

His thoughts reverted to the south country again. The wolves had been there too. They called them lobos or buffalo wolves; but they were the same wicked, brave, wild killers, with the same uncanny instinct for survival. They had finally been poisoned off, but perhaps—who knows?—an odd one might still stray east from the foothills or north from the Missouri breaks or the Musselshell. So many different ways to go unseen, he had thought, for cattle. Didn't this apply also to lobos—and cattle thieves?

The horse traders, now. He really knew nothing about them. But come to think of it, hadn't Jasper at the stopping house said they had come from that part of Montana—the Musselshell River? That was a country with a tradition of mustangers, wild-horse hunters. But that name sometimes meant people who were not too scrupulous between wild and "gentle" stock, between branded horses and slicks.

He'd only seen the horse traders once—in town. At first sight you might think they were putting on a show à la Western movie bad men; they had narrow dark faces, sideburns, black hats ("baddy" hats!), jingling spurs. But you'd be wrong. He doubted if they had ever seen a movie, but the Hollywood spotters had seen men like them! These fellows could ride and they could rope. They had guts, and like the wolves they might be close when you thought them miles away. The Man himself had seen tracks on the game-trails more than once. Tracks which fitted the hooves of none of his mounts, and too well trimmed to have been left by a wild one.

Come to think of it, he hadn't seen his own brood-mares for nearly two weeks. They had some good following fillies, and their foals would be coming any time. They ranged between Wild Horse Point and the Salt Springs. He must find time to look them over; but mares had little trouble foaling as a rule, while the calving cows needed his attention—and the Boy's—right now. Perhaps tomorrow, or the next day . . .

It was three days later that he rode north. He didn't find the mares up Salt Springs way, but he did find a saddle-horse track, and a place where it had grazed at least an hour, and then, pushed into an anthill, a couple of hand-rolled cigarette stubs. Who had rested there? And what had he been looking for? Or who had he waited for? Damn! Well, come on, Fox.

The Man topped the ridge and rode down into the west valley, where he could see the gleam of the Middle Fork. Something moved among the ground-birch scrub on the flat. It was one of his mares. The herd ran together at his approach, whinnying and nuzzling their new foals. There were three of these already.

He rode slowly and easily towards them, letting Fox snatch at the grass every few steps. Now he sat quietly, his leg hooked over the saddle-horn, and rolled a cigarette. The mares began to come towards him, as they always did. But shyly, reluctantly. He spoke to them. "Come on, Julie, tell me what happened?" But Julie, relaxed by his voice, only dropped her head to the green grass. No doubt about it, they had been spooked. They were still ready to fly at any quick movement. He noticed that one mare limped, and was able to see that she had a dry spruce snag near her stifle joint, on the inside. They looked muddy and scratched, and one of the roans had part of a spruce branch entangled in her long mane.

Most of the spruce country was north of here, he thought. These horses had been run—run hard. Whether by wolves or men, that was anyone's guess. But a bunch of gentle old mares aren't easy to chase off their home range, thank goodness.

He paid good money for the lease of his range and didn't mind who rode across it; but confound it, the custom was to drop in and have coffee and a chat—not to ride around unseen!

The Man shrugged, crushed out his own cigarette stub, unhooked his leg from the saddle-horn, and started the bunch for home. They went around Wild Horse Point as if the devil were after them, crossed the creek with a grunt and a splash, and trotted down the hay-trail to the corral, manes tossing and wet tails flying.

This wasn't their usual sedate walk-trot at all. You would think they were broncs, rather then sedate old ex-pack-horses! He remembered that the mustangers were supposed to chase any horses they met with, just to make them wild. That way they were easier to drive! Something nasty beat behind his eyes all the way to the corral. There he roped the roan and tied one front foot up. It took all his strength and a good pair of pliers to pull out the snag. The pain brought her to her knees. She must have been running all out to send that dry piece of wood so deep. As soon as the snag came out the festering wound began to run, and the awful smell nearly choked him. He realized he was none too soon, as he daubed the wound with pine tar.

The rest of the summer passed peacefully enough. There were forty-five acres of oat hay this year, and some of it held pretty good grain too. The garden was extra good. They had done so well with peas last year that they'd sown a lot more this spring. It was the best land for peas he had ever seen, though beans didn't do so well. The spring frosts always caught them.

The Woman and the Kid shelled peas every night for weeks, laying them on tarps to dry, and by fall had nearly a sackful. There'd be no shortage of good pea-soup for winter.

Weaning time came. The cattle were corralled and the calves separated and put in the weaning paddock, where there was water where they were fed from the stacks alongside.

The cows, turned out on the range, hung about for a week, bawling in answer to the calves' long and bereaved chorus. The Man said this was the rancher's best music, his orchestra. But the Woman said she preferred the gramophone, and kept the machine busy with Bach and Beethoven, trying to drown out the calves. Nobody won.

Finally only an occasional cow would come tearing back from feeding on the hillside to stare and roar through the stout spruce-log fence of the weaning quarters, and before long peace reigned once more at Deep Springs.

The cows drifted off, and as soon as snow got too deep for them to graze, they were fed daily in the spruce grove half a mile south. Too bad about cattle, the Man used to say. If only they could paw like horses, what a lot of work you would be saved—but a cloven hoof was no good for that, and unlike buffalo, cattle didn't care to root in the snow with their muzzles. No matter how much grass lay under the snow, if they couldn't

see it, it might as well not be there. They did browse quite a bit, of course, nipping off fine twigs like moose, but that wasn't enough.

The Man rode often that winter to watch his mares. They were settling down again. It was on one of these rounds—in November—that the Man located the bear den. It was a male, and males don't always sleep so early or so deeply as she-bears. This one was evidently not satisfied with his bed, for the Man saw his tracks leaving an oat-hay stack, where bruin had been munching on the grain, and saw also the scattered straws showing that he carried back bedding.

The Man caught up to the animal, dragging the mass of straw, and shot it within a few yards of the den. Fox hated to be loaded with the hams and hide, and carried his burden with many a snort and many a rolling backward glance which showed the white of his eye.

Here was that "plenty grease" of which Old Mary had spoken once, for the he-bear carried almost three inches of fat on his broad back. The Woman would have a busy few days "rendering" and bottling the grease. It made the finest shortening for pies and pastries—colourless, odourless, and tasteless.

Another winter settled in, with time to read and to relax. It took barely five hours a day to feed the barn stock, the calves, and the range cattle. In February, with longer days there would be next year's wood to cut and haul; but now the big heater, made from a forty-five-gallon gasoline barrel, crackled and spat, the coal-oil lamps glowed softly yellow, and—let the trees crack like rifles in the frost, let the wind swirl the snow, drifting it in the open, coiling it around the house like a serpent—the people in the house cared little.

The Kid did his home-work in a corner. Small, upstairs, slept. The Boy braided a pair of raw-hide bridle-lines. The Woman and the Man took turns to read aloud, and before bed-time the teacups rattled.

Chapter 11

Next spring the Man made a deal for a few more cows, for he had plenty of range and was required to have so many head of stock per acre to hold his lease. He planned for five hundred head eventually, but if he did not control enough land at the start there was the danger of being surrounded, as he had been years ago on the prairies, by settlers who would themselves go broke on too-small holdings, and at the same time ruin him by preventing him from expanding. It was an old pattern he did not want to see repeated; and he knew there were people to whom a paltry ten or twenty acres of agricultural land would look good. In a couple of years they would throw up their hands in despair.

There was still some snow in the bush, but the sidehills and small prairies were now clear. Several calves had already been dropped, when the weather unexpectedly turned colder in the first week in April. For some reason, just as daylight began to appear, the Man was thinking of wolves. He could not sleep, but dressed and went to the kitchen to make a cup of tea. As he sipped, his mind went back over the years, and he thought of that day in the Pasquia Hills when his sleigh dogs had howled and rattled their kennel-chains. . . . He had gone out in time to see a doe, heavy with young, stumbling towards him. Her flanks were heaving and her tongue was out as she fought for breath. Disregarding him she walked down the bank of Carrot River—now flowing free of spring ice—behind him. Into the water she went until it was almost over her back, and stood there panting. The sun showed the noon hour before she finally returned to shore and began to browse. He knew she had been run by wolves; that somehow she guessed the grey killer would not venture too close to man . . .

At that moment he heard a cow bawl from Round Hill Prairie, not half a mile south. Then another . . . and another. . . . The sound was shrill in his ears.

Setting down his cup with a clatter, the Man hurried to the barn, saddled Fox, thrust his rifle in its scabbard, and mounted.

The unthawed patches of snow crunched frostily under Fox's hooves, and the Man swore, thinking how noisy his approach was bound to be.

Topping the last low knoll he faced the prairie where the cow-herd had bedded. Several cows stood over their calves. One old lead-cow was slowly climbing the slope of Round Hill, which abutted from the ridge at this point. She went without hurry, and one by one all the cows—except those with calves—began to leave their beds and file after her.

This looked normal, a mere morning change of grazing grounds, for cattle rarely feed where they bed.

Just then a young cow, suckling her sleek black calf, looked towards the bush on the south. Then she bawled angrily. The other mothers did likewise and drew a little closer together. The Man, sitting his saddle quietly, rifle now in the crook of his arm, heard an answering bellow from the buildings. It was the Angus bull from his corral, and he rumbled and grumbled between roars.

Even Fox stopped champing on his bit and braced himself for the expected shot.

Then came a soft crunch-crunch on the snow among the tangled willows, and the Man saw the merest shadow move and disappear. Crunch-crunch—another shadow, a mere wraith.

Wolves. The crunch was not sharp enough for deer.

His rifle cocked, the Man waited. No point in shooting blindly. All was now perfectly quiet; the few cows gathering in a tight knot, staring south; the old lead-cow quickening her pace and now disappearing over the hill.

He touched Fox and rode slowly around the cows and calves. They were relaxing.

The wolves had got his scent, he knew.

He circled again, showing himself, talking to the cows. They began to graze. He dismounted and twice left his sign, pungent with man-smell, on the tree trunks, claiming his territory as a wolf does. It was an old trick.

"That may hold them," he said to Fox, as he mounted and started off after the rest of the bunch.

It is remarkable how fast cattle can walk when they have the will. When overthirsty, when a storm threatens, or when bulls hear a cow call in a certain way, then they can cover a good four miles an hour. But when just drifting, or when driven, they rarely exceed half that pace. So it was that the moving cattle were already over a mile away, "stringing right along," as he'd say, by the time the Man topped the crest of the hill. He could see the rear-guard winding along down the centre of the ridge, outlined against the growing light.

He urged Fox on as soon as the horse had regained his breath from the climb. Then a slight movement caught his eye, a mere flick of the tail, from behind an immense rock six feet high and weighing many tons. He rode to it, to find a heifer licking her minutes-old calf, the placenta still falling over her hocks like an Indian's bright blanket.

"Sho—old girl." The Man smiled. "Little 'un, eh?" The heifer raised mild, proud eyes and returned to her licking.

He left her. He knew she was safe for the moment. She must have slipped aside unseen as labour caught up to her. The calf would give off no tell-tale scent as yet. A wolf might pass by on the other side and never know.

But a little farther on the Man saw the pug-marks of wolves in the cattle's tracks. During the short delay the herd had disappeared from sight. At first he thought they had scattered, but no—the tracks went straight on. They must have gone over the point. He was close now to where the ridge narrowed and then slid abruptly down. He could see across the creek to ridge after blue ridge rising to the mountains themselves.

He could see the shadowed gash beyond the creek, which was the canyon.

A sound below made him withdraw his gaze from those distant prospects. Looking to the right he saw the roan lead-cow steadily walking in his direction again, weaving through the unleafed brush of the low ground, and followed by the others.

The foxy old girl! She had led over the point, turned sharp around at the foot, and was making back to Round Hill Prairie by the wagon-trail. She knew wolves would not attack a moving herd in close formation. They would simply trail along, as they had followed the buffalo herds in days gone by, awaiting the time the cattle would scatter out to feed. Then it would be easy to cut off one and surround it. But now the sun was high. Hunting time was over. The wolves had lost heart, had sensed that man was about.

At the moment the Man arrived at that conclusion, he heard a cheated howl from the direction of the badlands which faced the canyon.

The cattle demanded a lot of attention that summer. For some reason, instead of feeding mainly on the flats they chose to graze exclusively south and west from Wolf Point, downstream, among the grassy hillsides of the deeper valley of Cutbank Creek itself.

The Man blamed this on the newly acquired cows trying to work their way towards their former home on the river, for each day they wandered farther, as if they knew the creek must take them there. Why they did not take the shorter upland trail he could not guess. So every few days he had to work them back, for cows had to be "range broke" in a land where no fences existed for many miles. And except for his crop-land and the small horse pasture at the ranch, the nearest barbed wire was all of twenty miles away.

Day after day—and haying time was nearly upon them—the Man or the Boy had to disappear over the rim-rock and follow the crooked, winding waterway, which looped back and forth, leaving small grassy meadows now to this side, now to that, necessitating a crossing each time; for where there was a meadow the water, on the other side, always flowed beneath a high, crumbling cutbank full of snags and fallen trees on its crest.

Each night the cattle were brought back to Wolf Point. Since Atchikoos had scared the wolves from there, the cattle had had little fear of the place. In fact, that summer, since the cattle

became accustomed to bedding below the point, the men built a branding corral of logs to avoid driving the cows and calves the extra two miles to the ranch headquarters.

So it was that one day, not wishing to bring the cattle back in the dark when it was easy to lose one or more in the brush, the Man took sandwiches for two days, as well as a tea pail.

It was as well that he did so, for it was dusk before he found the herd, which had travelled farther than usual, kept on the move by the hordes of mosquitoes. The day had been hot. So hot that down here out of the breeze both man and horse were wet with sweat all mixed with blood from insect bites.

He heard a scuffle in the bush. He saw two bear cubs up a tree, at the foot of which their mother, a large brute, stood upright like a man, her snout drawn back to clear her long teeth, her clawed front paws ready. She growled—if a bear's loud, hissing expulsion of breath can be called a growl.

Fox stood still. He knew the game: the raised rifle, three shots, and three deaths. The Man felt a pang of regret, for he had respect for wild creatures. But this was nature, the survival of the fittest. Already he had lost three calves to bears this year. There were too many bears around. Why, only the year before at berry-time he had seen what he thought were seven head of cattle below him in a small opening. They were lying down, four blacks and three reds, coloured like his cows. He had ridden down, only to find they were bears. He hadn't expected to see them like that—they are more apt to be solitary.

Quickly the Man skinned the she-bear, looping the hide over a limb. He would pick it up later.

The creek banks became steeper at every mile, the south side heavily timbered, the north (or sunny) side covered in short grass and sage, representing what a biologist would call two quite different life-zones. Sometimes on the north there were shale-cliffs so steep that, seeing three mule deer bound across, the Man wondered why they did not slide to the bottom, as did the mass of shale they dislodged at every bound.

An eagle screamed overhead, and he saw her bulky nest, topping a shale-pillar, held by a twisted ground-juniper.

Twice he might have shot a coyote, but those little silvery wolves did no damage. Dead stock, mice, and rabbits sufficed for them.

The Man knew he was near the cattle long before he broke from a patch of scrubby poplar cover into an open meadow. He caught the smell of them, rank on the hot, still air. So did Fox, who quickened his pace.

The herd lay close grouped in the lush grass, calves at their mothers' flanks.

Quickly he made a count. All there. He breathed a sigh of relief.

He did not bother to picket Fox, of the sorrel coat and sober blazed face; he had never been known to leave a camp.

The owls were hooting by the time the Man had brewed his tea, munched his sandwiches, and laid his head on his saddle, his chaps under him, his hairy saddle-blanket for covering.

The herd grunted softly, letting out great gusts of scented breath, their heads to their flanks. They would not move till dawn. Then they would want to walk.

Chapter 12

The Black Wolf rose from uneasy sleep, as a fox barked on the ridge above. He lay a hundred yards above the den in a patch of bear-berry, where he had been sleeping off a heavy meal. He had killed a foal two days before. He had run the mare along the left rim of the canyon, crowding her to the edge. In her desperation to shield the foal, she had kept between it and the danger. Closer and closer to the edge the wolf had driven her, until a break in the ground had made the little fellow lose his footing. Over it had gone.

The mare had whinnied in vain and turned back, but disregarding her, the Black Wolf, too, had launched himself into the depths below, and soon his teeth had been at the foal's throat. Tearing at it, he had filled his belly. He had soon been joined by his three-footed wife, and from time to time one or the other had slipped back to the den, to the pups lying in the dark, to regurgitate a half-chewed mass which the pups had attacked with miniature growls.

Now it was time to kill again.

The Black Wolf rose slowly, yawned to show his wicked dog-teeth, then stretched front and hind legs in turn. Turning his nose briefly towards the den to see that all was well, he trotted around the canyon shoulder to higher ground. The move to the canyon from Wolf Point had proved a lucky one. No rider had ever invaded this new sanctuary, nor approached within half a mile.

Now cow-smell was strong on the air. Daylight was near. Only a quarter of a mile from the canyon he stopped. He saw the cattle in the meadow below. Saw them rise one by one; first to their knees, then to their hind feet, finally to all fours. Calves, rested and hungry, butted their mothers with a smacking of lips which the wolf could hear, which made his own dark jowls drool.

He trotted calmly down the twisting game-trail which led to the meadow. Then he halted.

There was horse-smell too. And worse, smoke-smell. He saw a pin-point of flame in the dawn gloom. A point that burst into a strong, steady glow, smoke billowing upward.

The wolf made a half circle. He was as suspicious now as he had been confident a moment ago. He heard a cow leave the bunch and go down the creek bank; heard her cloven hooves click on gravel. He sat on his haunches, watching the camp, himself lost in shadow. He watched the Man boil his tea, watched him stamp out the fire and saddle Fox, whose white blaze showed strangely in the half-light. Then the Man picked up what looked like a stick, something he slung under the saddle-flap.

A slight morning breeze came towards the wolf, fluttering through the leaves and grass, and with it the smell he had first known on that night when he had released his mate's foot. The smell of those things he had found on his trails; those things which went off with a clack, upon which he had urinated in fury.

The smell of metal.

The Black Wolf fled silently. Not far. Only to the canyon's rim.

He was hungry. He remembered the cow down the bank. Perhaps the Man would go . . .

The cattle were walking well, stringing out ahead of the Man, who urged them on. The morning was cool, and even the calves trotted easily at their mothers' flanks. They had made nearly two miles, and soon they would want to graze.

The sun was well over the crest of the deep valley when the cattle scattered out across another meadow of perhaps seven acres. The Man started to ride around, counting his cattle. Once the count came wrong, then right again. Then wrong. Yes, he decided, he was one cow short. One of the three-year-olds which hadn't calved yet. She would be the last, and he didn't care for late calves.

Well, he would wait half an hour. Anything left behind usually followed. He'd give her a chance to catch up.

He was positive last night's tally had been right. Cattle are easy to count when they are lying down.

The sun rose higher, banishing the early vapours already risen from the creek and from the dew-wet grass. High on the point of a sugar-loaf butte a mule deer flicked her big ears and looked towards a patch of snowberry close by. Her fawn or fawns lay there, the Man guessed.

Two red-billed mergansers swept croaking around the bend and lit on the creek with a splash which set the spotted sandpipers teetering on the rocks and fluting musically.

The waiting man could hear the summer breeze playing in the shaggy spruce of the south bank, but here all was still. Only the cattle, tearing grass in great mouthfuls, curling their tongues about the tufts, disturbed that deep stillness. Mosquitoes swarmed in the humid air, covering the black cows with a freckling of grey, keeping the animals' tails switching and curling over their backs.

Between mouthfuls the big black bull strolled from cow to cow, testing, rumbling softly in his dewlapped throat. The calves were curled up in the grass close together, only their ears flickering back and forth against the stinging hordes. It was a peaceful scene. Black cattle in a green valley. Flesh and green grass. All flesh is grass, the Man thought. Even his. Even that of the wolves. Were it not so, this would be a Garden of Eden indeed. He saw the water, sparkling and hurrying over the pebbles, through dark pools, to its mysterious tryst with the sea; a yellow warbler singing, piercingly sweet, from the feathery willows; a chunky fox-sparrow sending his crystal-clear notes to echo from a cutbank. The little meadow was so peaceful, so isolated, so untouched by man over forgotten ages. Yet there was a serpent. An enemy. Or was *he*, the Man, the real enemy?

A twig snapped sharply, interrupting his reverie. It was not the laggard heifer he waited for, but only a young buck, its sprouting antlers heavy with velvet. It gazed mild-eyed at the cattle and slipped down the creek bank to drink.

Just then came a high, long-sustained bawl from far to the rear. The heifer. And in trouble. This was no call to rejoin the bunch, but that half scream he knew so well. The black bull raised his wet muzzle and crashed through the willows with an answering bellow of rage. The rest of the cattle stopped feeding, began to gather together, and a low muttering, as of distant thunder, ran through the bunch.

The Man barely touched Fox with the spur, and they raced back along the trampled trail, where already the grass was beginning to rise. At dead gallop he pulled his rifle from the scabbard and laid it in the crook of his arm, ready.

He was almost back at last night's camp, when he met the cow head-on. She was walking steadily, swinging her head a little. She looked all right, and the Man, relieved, quartered around her in the bush, his eyes on the back trail, his rifle ready. A wolf might be following . . .

Not a sight of one. Not a sound but the cow's split hooves clicking as she walked.

"Might as well take her back to the bunch," the Man thought. "Probably scared the wolf off with my mad gallop."

He turned Fox around. Then for the first time he saw the heifer from behind, and cursed aloud at the sight. "The black bastard!"

Her rear end was a mass of raw meat, blood oozing thick and dark to her hocks. Part of an unborn calf's front leg with its soft cream-coloured hoof dangled and swung beside her tail. Wolf work at its most hideous.

The heifer must have felt the birth-pangs last night and moved away from the bunch in search of that hidden privacy which motherhood demands. And the timber wolf had simply made a quick dash as she lay in pain, tearing at her before she could rise to her knees. Not waiting to kill.

Fox to this day showed in his round quarters a dimple you could put your fist in. A wolf had torn a couple of pounds of meat from him as a foal. Not many, attacked like that, survived. But no tendon had been torn, and Fox's mother was no fool . . .

As the Man read the story, he concluded it to be the work of one wolf only. As she got to her knees and started along the trail he must have kept behind her. It was as the wolf had slashed at her that she had bawled. The wolf had evidently seized hold of the half-born calf by its hanging head, for this was torn off, as well as one leg.

The cow might walk many miles yet. She would not stiffen up and become immobilized until she lay down to rest. Evidently, as with Fox, no tendons had yet been cut; but she must die eventually, and lingeringly.

The heifer stopped to crop at a tangle of sweet vetch, and at that moment the rifle left the Man's arm for his shoulder. There was a sharp crack, and she fell, drilled through the brain.

The bull bellowed high and long as the echoes of the shot rolled up and down the deep valley, sending the eagle screaming from her nest.

"That black bastard of a wolf must be denned down this way since Atchikoos put a scare into him," the Man confided to Fox, who flicked one ear in reply.

Without being reined, the sorrel turned back towards the canyon, the Man looking intently for signs. Not much chance of a shot now. Shouldn't have fired in a hurry. Scared the brute off. Yes, I should, though—oh hell—couldn't let the poor old girl walk around like that.

Soon he found the wide pug-marks he was looking for, and a calf's yellow foot. But no head. If it was carried off—perhaps a den! And then another set of tracks. He dismounted and hunkered down, rolling a smoke. The three-footed bitch! So, they were still around, that pair.

But search the canyon as he might, he found no den. The sides were a jumble of rocks and twisted, gnarled ground-juniper, and rocks show no tracks, although he slipped and scraped the yellow lichen off one big, flat-topped one.

With a final angry curse he climbed to where he had left Fox, mounted, and left the sun-heated cliff to the eagles and its own bloody secret, swearing by all the gods of war to return and find that den.

A week later he did.

He passed the carcass of the cow. Coyotes, foxes, and ravens had pretty well finished her. How quickly a dead animal becomes nothing but dried and stinking hair and white rib-bones. But no wolf had been there. Of that he was sure. Odd . . .

He found the den, its mouth hidden by juniper twigs, below that very flat-topped rock on which he had slipped. But it was empty, the latest sign a week old.

Once more the Black Wolf and his crippled mate had outmanoeuvred him.

Chapter 13

The Black Wolf and his wife carried their litter of pups around the corner of the buttes to a patch of fallen spruce. Here, above Thunder Creek, was an old den which had been dug by the Black Wolf's parents.

That rifle shot near the canyon had alerted the two wolves, and that scraped rock above the den had brought them to the realization that they had to move again. It was five miles to the new site, and it took all night for the wolf and his lame wife to make the double trip, each with a small, short-snouted bundle of fur held by the scruff. Finally the four pups lay in the cool darkness, once more by their mother's flank.

At dawn the Black Wolf made another of his clever kills. He could not run a fat buck alone, and passed up the one he saw, but by chance the new man who had just settled on Yellow Creek had let a gentle mare wander. To force her two-day-old foal over a cutbank had not been hard.

The young pups now came out to play in the dusk. They rolled each other over, nipping at each other's tails and ears, and tried their voices in short gruff barks and whines. It would be some months yet before they could achieve the Black Wolf's loud roar.

By September they began to join their mother on short forays. They found a dead moose and fed for a while on its carcass, but also learnt to dig out nests of young mice, and once—between them—they killed a rabbit, its warm blood whetting their keen appetites.

They learnt the sweetness of saskatoon fruit, the bitterness of wild cherries, and the pungent flavour of the high-bush cranberries which grew between the trees on the deep slopes of the creek bank.

For the rest of that summer and fall the Black Wolf avoided the vicinity of Deep Springs and the rancher who lived there. Some deep inner caution told him that here was a dangerous enemy; one who rode his range constantly, who had a knack of getting into the roughest and most inaccessible places.

The Man's stock rarely found their way around the buttes for more than a mile, but the new settler to the east, on Yellow Creek, had a few cattle unused to the bush. From his small herd and the many deer which roamed the hills the wolves fared well enough. However, nothing but bad luck attended the move to the buttes. The three-footed bitch, no weight-carrier at any time as a result of her disability, had somehow strained herself and had been short of milk. The pups, active enough, were not as well-grown as they should have been, nor as alert.

Another settler came in the fall too, seven miles up on Thunder Creek; a man with two sons, able youths and good shots. And then, a few weeks after, still another young rancher built his cabin west of Big Prairie, at a bend of the Elk-Run River.

After taking a calf and a yearling from the Yellow Creek man, the wolves next tackled one of his cows, pulling her down as she was drinking. She lay half-in, half-out of the creek, and as they started to tear at her belly they heard the settler ride up, and made off. When they returned just before dawn, one pup stepped in a trap. The rest never returned to that carcass.

Another of the youngsters, on a raid even farther east, ventured by night onto the Yukon Highway, to find itself full in the headlights of a truck. Dazzled and able only to see the road ahead, the young wolf ran uncertainly, dodging from side to side on the gravel road. The driver, with thoughts of the bounty spurring him on, finally succeeded in running him over. He threw the flattened body in his vehicle and proceeded on his way.

Within a month the other two pups had wandered off. Both fell victims to poison before the winter was over.

That was a winter of routine for the Man and the family. Feeding cattle. Hauling firewood. There were now a hundred acres of cultivated land under the snow, fifty acres seeded down to brome grass and alfalfa or timothy and alsike clover, the rest ready for crops in the spring.

A new horse-stable was built by Christmas, and the first dug-out barn, with its roof of hay and sod, was used only for the milk cow and the chickens.

The men visited both the new neighbours and told them of the Black Wolf, offering fifty dollars' bounty to whoever shot or caught him.

The Woman, too, had now the chance of occasionally seeing another of her sex besides Old Mary, Atchikoos' squaw.

The wild horses were getting to be a problem. They fed in spring only on the best grass, the good short grass of the hill-sides. Barely did the slopes green-up than the bands scattered over them, nipping the grass much shorter than cattle would, trampling the turf in wet weather so that when the sun came hot its blistering rays shrivelled the exposed root-stocks. The Man well knew that you can raise three head of cattle for one horse, and that each of these marauders was costing him pounds of beef and spoiling his range for the future, for grass too closely grazed grew up to bush and weeds. So whenever a band of horses was seen, one or other of the men would saddle up and chase them off. Fox liked that, but he was getting old and stiff now, and more and more the Man rode the young crop-eared buckskin, Ted.

The Cow Moose had a single calf again this year. She left it lying in the long grass as she fed. On the wind there came a sound of galloping from the south, and she trotted to her calf, nudged it with her big nose, and together the two melted into a willow thicket. The cow looked and listened, nostrils wide, ears pricked forward. The rumble came closer. Then into view came the troop of mares and young horses. They were running all out, ears back, tails flying, dodging and weaving between the clumps of scrub. Behind came the Man on the tall buckskin, and while the wild mares steamed sweat, this horse showed hardly dampness on his neck and flanks.

The Cow Moose turned sharply, lumbering down the hill, crashing among the bushes. Almost simultaneously the buckskin reared and turned, bucking.

The Man jerked on the lines and got his mount's head up. "What the devil ails you, Ted?" he rasped, turning him again to the chase.

What he saw then, what had frightened Ted, was a sort of square of black and white, gleaming in the sun. Ted tried to buck again. The Man rubbed his eyes as he controlled the snorting, sideling horse. The moose still crashed somewhere below. What on earth was this thing? It looked like a checkerboard road sign!

Then it moved. The Man laughed. The horse whinnied, and his ears—which had been back—sprang forward. Why, it was nothing but two big pinto horses, head to tail, which had stood rooted in amazement at the sight of the galloping troop. The Man rode closer. He could see they were old stagers—a broke work-team. Mares. He had seen them before on a wagon in the settlements. Old Swanson's pintos! What were they doing here? Even if Swanson didn't want them any more for ploughing, they still had many years to raise colts.

Perhaps the horse traders. Stocking their range . . .

Quietly the Man worked Ted around them and started them for the home corral.

Damn these . . . suspicions . . .

He'd drop a note to Swanson.

April weather suddenly changed. The wind blew from the north, bringing cold and snow, while the thermometer dropped to near zero for several nights. The prairie chickens, which had started their spring dancing, suddenly stopped and came in hundreds to the tall poplars by the buildings, climbing and fluttering among the branches to feed on the swelling buds. This was a sign of more bad weather. The small pools froze over. The riders had to revert to winter chaps and sheepskin coats, mitts and fur caps. For ten days it was a nightmare locating the well-scattered cattle, some already as far away as the buttes. Calves were coming fast. They had to take hay on pack-horses to inaccessible places where cows stood over their calves in the deep snow, for they could not make milk on twigs and other browse. Many calves were brought to the corral on saddles, slung over the rider's knees, the cow following; but many a young heifer did not know enough to follow the rider, for the scent of the calving bed was strong and she would hurry back to that. Besides, her instinct had taught her that her calf belonged on the ground, and she would not look up for it. In such cases the rider would prod the calf, causing it to bleat. This usually did the trick and made the heifer, full of anxiety, follow close behind the rider.

One morning the Man found a calf with its ears already frozen, and so chilled it was doomed to die. He lifted it to the saddle and rode home. Ted was getting used to these double burdens. Leaving the cow eating hay in the corral, the Man carried the wet, leggy youngster to the house, dumped it by the kitchen stove, and stood pulling the long icicles from his moustache.

The Woman had made tea. "Let's try it on the calf," said the Kid.

The Man looked in admiration. "Just the thing!" he said.

They poured two cups of warm, sweet tea down the calf's throat. It sneezed and shook its damp head, but in five minutes it stopped shivering under the gunny-bags they had been rubbing it with, and in half an hour the Man took it to the corral and had the satisfaction of watching it wobble to its mother's flank, spread its big knees, find a full teat, and take a more natural breakfast.

Its badly frozen ears and tail fell off shortly, and ever after—under the name of "Teacup"—it could be easily recognized among its mates.

When the weather finally warmed up it did a good job. The snow melted rapidly, leaving pools everywhere. It was hot, and one heifer with the fever of labour on her stood panting in one of the pools, dropping her calf in a foot and a half of water.

That's how the Man found them on his rounds—the calf already drowned, the mother nudging it, trying to make it get up. Her bag was badly swollen, and he had to rope her and let some of the milk out.

Truly, the range-cattle business had its hazards. Cattle, like people, differed. That heifer would go for beef in the fall; bad, stupid mothers begat stupid daughters. Survival of the fittest worked here just as much as elsewhere.

Chapter 14

A fire was coming over the ridge. It burnt fiercely in the willow clumps, more slowly in the patches of down timber—the criss-cross patches which were themselves the harvest of a much earlier fire.

The Man rode up the ridge to watch it. Cattle were slowly working south from the flickering flames and smoke. They had little fear of these spring fires (which never "crowned" in the trees) but easily evaded them. The Man had little objection to them either. There were usually snowdrifts still left in the coulees, and the fires rarely got out of hand but actually improved the range by helping to keep down the smaller brush and causing the wild peas scattered among the dead leaves to sprout more abundantly. Autumn fires were different. They burnt into the hot, dry ground.

But this time the Man heard a muffled bawl from deep within a patch of fallen logs. He turned Ted towards the sound. The air was getting uncomfortably hot, although the fire approached slowly, working its way from log to log, helped by the matted clumps of dry grass between them.

He found the yearling trapped by one hind foot which had slipped between two heavy logs. It must have been enticed into this tangle by the tender blades of young grass just sprouting. Frightened by the smoke and heat, the animal was completely bewildered. If it had known enough to back up a little it could have pulled its leg free.

By the time the Man was able to free the panicked beast, the fire was really close. But the yearling only blundered towards the approaching fire, where it roared in a clump of dry willows, so he heel-roped it and dragged it out by the hind legs. The yearling bawled in protest as it came bumping over the logs. Bumpety-bump for a hundred yards, the fire getting hotter, sparks singeing its hair and making Ted flinch. Out in the open the Man removed the rope. The yearling got to its feet as the rope came Thwack! on its rump, and it trotted south to join its mates.

And so another name was born. Shadrach went to market a year and a half later, but the marks of the steer's escape were as good as a brand: a raking scar from shoulder to hip, made by a spruce knot over which he had been dragged. As for the Man's moustache and eyebrows—they were renewable.

Yet in spite of frost, snow, water, wolves, and fire the herd was rapidly increasing.

The Man got a heavy tractor that summer. A John Deere "D" model, which he "walked" up the trail in two days. In several places he had to widen the road to take the big wheels, but the weather was dry, the soft spots hard, and the fords shallow with good gravel footing. Most of the more open, brushy land was now broken, and the rest of the flat had some pretty large trees spotted in bluffs and clumps, the stumps of which a horse-drawn plough could not budge. He still had nearly three hundred acres to break, and the cattle could not increase more rapidly than his capacity to feed them in winter. That summer the tractor was hardly still for a day, one of the men operating it while the other, assisted by the Kid, cut and piled trees and willow brush.

For haying they had, too, a hay-loader which, dragged behind the wagons, put on a load in short order.

When haying was done, or in wet spells between operations, the newly broken land had to be disked and worked down, and the roots picked and burnt. New land is not easily made, and working hard at it, the Man welcomed the mid-afternoon lunch which the Woman brought out daily. In one hand she carried her basket laden with bread and butter and cake and sealers of tea, by the other she led Small, who loved these expeditions. Kitty came in the rear, stepping gingerly upon the short, sharp hay stubble.

They had branded early that summer. Since the wolves had moved again the cattle fed less in the Cutbank valley but had taken more to the west country, the swamp across the creek, and the flats around Wild Horse Point, so the corral at Wolf Point was not used. Instead, the cattle were rounded up and brought home. The neighbour boys from Thunder Creek came to help. All day the work went on, the men coughing in the dry dust and the smoke which drifted around them from the branding fire.

The Kid tended the irons, running from the fire to the workers with a hot iron when called, running back with the cold one to reheat it. The Boy roped the calves by the heels, the Thunder Creek boys wrestled them down, throwing the loop back to the roper, and the Man pressed the hot LADDER s on their glossy ribs.

Finally, over a good supper of roast bear-cub and saskatoon pie made with bear-grease shortening, the men could hear the bawling of calves and the lowing of cows as they "mothered off" after being separated in the recent melee. Good-nights were said, the Thunder Creek boys mounted and rode east over the ridge, and peace reigned.

Chapter 15

In September the Kid rode down the trail on Starlight. He was off to high school, a city boarding school, from which he would return only for brief summer holidays. It turned out that he was not, as his father had conjectured, the rancher type. He left Starlight in old Jasper's pasture and got a ride into the village.

Only a little later the Boy left. He had always wanted a soldier's or a sailor's life and had felt it keenly that he had been too young for Hitler's war. Now the Korean War was on, and he had made up his mind to join the Princess Pats.

This meant the Man had to hire help, and he was lucky to engage a lad, about the Boy's age, the son of a farmer at Beaverlodge. He was a good hand with machinery, and what he did not know of range work he would learn. And this left to the Man more time to what he loved best—riding.

It was several weeks before he found time to make the trip to the stopping house to pick up old Starlight, who had been left in the pasture there. He stayed just long enough to pay for the grazing, for he was in a hurry to get home before dark, and trotted pretty briskly. Two miles from the house was a pool in the bush, and when the horses turned their heads to it he let them have a drink. Both were sweating a little, but as a rule range-bred saddle-horses could be trusted not to take too big a fill. He sat rolling a cigarette when he realized that Starlight was gulping pretty steadily.

"Come on, you old idiot," he muttered, and pulling the horse's head up, turned again to the trail at a trot.

Before he had gone many yards he felt the lead-rope tighten and heard Starlight groan. He looked around and saw the old fellow rolling his eyes, sweat pouring from him and running down his hind legs. "Touch of colic," the Man thought, and slowed down. A colicky horse must be kept moving. Nevertheless he was brought to a stop by Starlight going to his knees and then rolling on his side. Try as he would, the Man could not get him up. Suddenly he thought of what that previous owner had said: "Watch his kidneys." It looked like blackwater. He left Starlight and raced for home.

The Woman met him. "Supper's ready—why, where's Starlight?"

"Cashing in, I'm afraid," he replied. "Get me that bottle of linseed oil, will you?" He went on. "And a couple of hot-water bags. I'll get some saddle-blankets."

Back by Starlight he hastily lifted the old horse's head and poured down the mixture of oil and turpentine. He got water from the pool, heated it in an old pail over a hastily made fire, and filled the water bags. Then he managed to heave Starlight into a more natural position, with his head up and his body blocked on one side by a piece of deadfall. If he couldn't get the old boy up, if he couldn't loosen those kidneys, Starlight would soon be a goner. Once he did get him up. Starlight staggered a few paces, spread his legs, and groaned without result. Down he went again.

All night the Man kept reheating the water, laying the bags over the horse's kidneys and covering them with piled-on saddle-blankets, and using one to mop the steamy sweat from legs and flanks, while the skin twitched and shuddered under his hands. Several times he got the horse up, led him in a short circle, but he always went down again, groaning.

It was nearly dawn when the old horse staggered to his feet and tried again. This time a triumphant flow rewarded him. Black, pungent, evil-looking.

Starlight's groans stopped. He no longer poured sweat. His

eye brightened, and he whinnied loud and clear, answered by a mutter from the grazing Ted.

"You old beggar!" said the Man, relief in his voice. "You had me plumb scared. Come on."

They took it easy going home. The horses were glad of their hay, Ted to get the saddle off; the Man gladder for coffee and bed.

The small one was a little girl now. She loved to pet any stock she could get her hands on. Old mother hen had passed on, but her daughters, a speckledy hen and two black ones (she called them the Dawn Sisters), were her favourites. Speckledy pecked every morning at the screen door to be let in the house. She clucked and talked in the kitchen but not for long. Soon she went under the sitting-room couch, from which she would emerge, cackling for her reward. Small gave her a crust and let her out before reaching under the couch for the brown egg she would have for breakfast next day.

Lillian the cat had also passed on to other hunting grounds, and Kitty was a new grey "Peace River cat." She was Small's constant companion on their walks, which were restricted to the five-acre house yard.

One day the Man, heading for the stockyard with a load of hay on the wagon, saw Small and Kitty by the slop pile at the edge of the spruce. He cleared up the pile each spring, but now there were assorted cans and bones there. He waved to the child and drove on to the barnyard behind the spruce. Leaving the team standing, he started for the house for tea. Small was by the house, looking back with coaxing sounds. Kitty, behind her, stood with tail fluffed up.

Then he saw the bear, glossy black, standing by the slop pile.

Quietly he turned back to the barn, his heart thumping, swept his rifle from its saddle scabbard, and ran quickly back, levering in a shell as he went. The bear was still looking at the child, and the Man heard her say: "Doggy, doggy!" just as he shot.

The bear fell. Small burst into tears. And over the teacups her father had to explain gently that the black animal was not a dog, but a bear—like those skins he often tacked on the woodshed. They didn't hunt people as a rule, he said, but getting too near made them feel cornered and they might hurt you.

"Remember that calf I brought in, all slashed on its side? The one I had to stitch up? I don't want to stitch *you* up, do I?" he explained. Small dried her eyes. She was a ranch child and knew about death.

She would have liked a dog. But dogs were a great nuisance around cattle. Always in the way. And if the cows got used to a dog, they'd be less alert against the wolves. Small would have to be content with her chickens, her cat, and Robin. For she was now learning to ride.

Small named everything. The cat was her Kitty-Kotty, the big tractor Sir Reginald Thumper from its slow two-cylinder explosions. The big black bull was Christopher because it resembled the photograph of her uncle, a bishop in Australia. Another bull was Sir Thomas More—why, nobody knew. The Dawn Sisters were, of course, the offspring of the Marquis of Dawn, the early crowing rooster. Two cows of rather ungainly appearance were the Ugly Sisters, and two others with lyre-shaped horns, respectively the Ugly and the Pretty Ankola. Small loved looking at books about Africa.

Riding the creek bank that night, the new lad from Beaverlodge heard the slap of a beaver's tail and saw that a dam was being built. The news was received with excitement.

"The one thing I missed," said the Man smilingly. "I saw beaver cutting away down near Jasper's last year. Guess some have moved up from there. According to Atchikoos, the Indians cleared them out some years back, but I guess they're building up again. With any luck they'll increase. Let's hope so."

Chapter 16

Soon the snow would fly again, and the beef had to go to market before that.

This meant another round-up of the herd, from which two dry cows, about fifteen two-year-olds, and a big steer—a three-year-old—were cut out. On last year's drive this steer had "quit the bunch" in the big timber of Thunder Creek. Rather than run it to death (as can happen with a "hot" animal) and rather than risk the others breaking, the Man had said: "Let him go! He'll walk back home." But the steer had not. After snow came he had found a bunch of wild horses pawing, and soon found he could push one aside with his horns and feed where the grass had been exposed. So he had wintered out quite happily with his kind hosts, and next spring had turned up with a bunch of cows. Now he was fat.

"Watch that steer," the Man warned the Thunder Creek boys, who had come to help. "He's a bunch-quitter!" The Man knew the animal had only to escape again and nothing short of a rifle bullet would ever make meat of him. "When we get to Thunder Creek timber, boys," he went on, "don't crowd them till I say. Till then I want them strung out. These dry cows will help steady them. But *watch that timber!* One of you ride that side, back a-ways. I'll be on point. And I don't want any shouting till we start up across the creek. Keep 'em cool and easy if you can. Once we get off their range, across the Thunder, we'll soon have 'em trail-broke. We'll camp as far east as we can get by sundown." The boys nodded.

The Man rode to the point. Old cows like something to follow. Besides, a man ahead ensured no wolves or bears on the trail to suddenly scatter the cattle in the brush. One Thunder Creeker rode on either flank, and the Lad brought up the rear—the drag, as cowmen would call it. Last of all came Robin carrying a light pack of blankets and grub, with an axe tucked under the diamond hitch.

The walk to the top of Thunder Creek was without incident, although the big steer looked longingly up at the ridge above the buttes, where he had wintered with his friends. As they started down the creek hill, with its jumble of deadfall, the riders were tense. No one talked. No one rolled a smoke. No one took eyes off the moving cattle. The big steer topped them all, easy to watch.

The Man on point kept one eye to the rear. He was not to let them crowd past him. He was not to get too far ahead. He had to wait at each curve of the trail to see they were following. The old cows, on the lead, came steadily on. They had no calves to think of, to worry about. They had often been down here to drink. But never up the other side. That would be the test. Man against love of the home range.

The Man spoke quietly. "When they get to the creek, let 'em drink if they want to but not for long. Don't let them scatter. Crowd them up tight. When I raise my hand you can let out a yell—get them going up the other side fast. Don't give them time to think. O.K.?" The boys nodded again.

At the tall timber the big steer suddenly made a dash to the right. But he hadn't seen a Thunder Creek rider slip quietly into the spruce, hadn't seen the lariat swinging gently. Just in the nick of time the heavy honda whacked the steer on his tender muzzle, and he wheeled back into the bunch, shaking his head. As the cattle began to drink at the creek he turned sharply around once more to get uphill, but the pack-horse, by no accident, was in his way, and he turned back as the Lad crowded him.

The Man on the far bank lifted his hand. Now, with a whoop, ropes swinging, the boys rushed the cattle at the bank and well up the steep trail. The two cows followed Ted steadily. The Man had, years before, learnt the advantage of having a few dry cows with a steer-herd. Steers still have enough male instinct to like the company of cows. Furthermore, they had always followed their mothers the first year, and then afterwards it was always an old cow that led them to fresh grazing grounds or water. If any steers break away, the cows can usually be kept steady by a good man, and form a rallying point towards which the breakers can be driven.

Several times, labouring up the steep hill, a steer would threaten to break, to plunge off the trail to the depths below. But the boys knew their job. They kept their eyes open and ropes trailing, ready to dash after a truant. They all gained the top and reached a level prairie across which the trail wound to the south-east. Another ten miles would take them to the first crossing of the Cutbank. Four miles from Thunder Creek they let the cattle feed; they would be thirsty soon and would walk willingly to the Cutbank.

Now they fed and lay down by turns. The big steer, after that crack on the nose, kept well in the centre of the bunch. It was four o'clock when he, the first to rise, snuffed towards the south-east. He wanted water.

"Let's go," said the Man.

Hastily the gear was packed on Robin. Crumbs were brushed from mouths, cinches tightened. The Man rode to the point. The boys roused what cattle still lay bedded.

They watered the cattle and crossed the creek to the far side, making camp right by the ford to be between the cattle and home, and leaving the Man on night guard, the boys slept. At midnight guard was changed, and by daybreak the drive was resumed. Two days later the bunch filed into the sales corral at the settlement, led by the big steer, who had apparently decided that when you couldn't beat them you might as well join them.

Eighteen head of cattle wasn't many, but the price was good. The Man's cheque was for over twenty-five hundred dollars. Not bad for a small outfit with expenses at a minimum! He paid his lease, made his land payments, and was satisfied. They could live another year, and next season he'd have all of twenty-five to sell, for his own heifers were now in production. Over sixty breeding cows.

Always next year . . .

When he returned from the drive, the Man found that two animals—a big calf and a yearling—had been killed in a night attack from the north. The Woman told him how she had lain all night listening to the bawling of cattle way up the valley. She and Small had shivered at the horrible wolf howls from the ridge as daylight broke.

Maddened, the Man rode all the way back to the settlement next day and had a talk with the game warden.

"Poison is the only answer," said that worthy, filling his pipe. "You're bound to get some. Better than traps. But mind you, poison only works once in an area. You get some, but you'll never get more for a long time. They're smart, those fellows, and the ones that don't get it are even smarter. I'll give you a permit so's you can get strychnine at the drugstore. An old horse is the best bait—or shoot one of those wild ones."

Back home the Man carefully prized up a board in the porch floor and packed the bottle of strychnine far in. Then he nailed the board back. He would know it by a knothole between two nails. He told nobody. He'd not use it unless he had to. His gesture was more symbolic than anything. He knew he was impulsive, but now his rage was lessening. Action always did that. How often did he write long, angry letters to newspapers about the things he didn't like! They never got posted. Looking at them two days later, he'd chuckle and poke them in the stove.

The Man was not satisfied with his cattle. Angus was a good breed, but they didn't climb the hills enough. There were miles of good range "up top," but the black cows grazed the valleys too close, and especially the hillsides. That was where the short grass grew, the only grass which cured for fall and winter grazing, but unless he could leave at least a 50 per cent carry-over it would soon change to grey sage and scrub, like the hillsides along the river which Jasper had "sheeped off." It took thirty acres to a cow in this country, but cattle should get the full advantage of summer grazing up top and in the bush, so the hills could rest.

The old-time cowmen used to say: "Time to worry about grass when it gets scarce." So they went broke, not heeding the signs. The time for him to worry, the Man knew, was *now.*

Herefords—good cattle too—would do no better.

He'd try a couple of Galloway bulls. These were hill-cattle, hardy, hornless. They'd keep the herd black. But the only two breeders in the West, when he wrote, told him all bull calves were bespoke for two years. The man at High River assured him he was not the only one who was feeling the results of the "shortening up" of the Angus by the show-breeding fraternity. Legs were too short. Bulls, raised on extra nurse cows, were too thickset and didn't get around the range. Then the Man told an old rancher friend at Manyberries about his trouble. Old Mac wrote: "Go get yourself a couple of West Highlanders. They'll do the job. They aren't too big, especially from Scotland —where they eat heather and mist. Out here they'll double their weight. They'll rustle in winter—eat browse like moose. They're chunky. I know. My dad had a Highland bull, and when it came to branding time those cross-bred calves sure had the weight! Ranchers came from Medicine Hat and Maple Creek to look at that long-horned rascal, but Dad didn't mind. I guess if it hadn't been for Kaiser Bill's war, which stopped all shipments, there'd have been a real run on Highlanders the next year or two. In the meantime, the Yanks were peddling their Herefords, and Alberta went White-face. There's a Jim Lindsay at Lloydminster who used to import Highlands. Give him a try. You'll find they've got hair like a door mat, and cold winds don't mean nothing to them."

Three young bulls accordingly arrived at the settlement by truck, were duly admired (or rather joked about—"That guy up in there's sure headed for broke!"), and sent on to be unloaded at Jasper's place. The Man and the Lad drove them to the ranch in two days behind a sleigh loaded with hay. They had coats like yaks, and their horns already showed promise

of being as long and curved as in the Farquharson prints so many Old Country people hung on their walls.

Now they were in the corral. They scared the hens, and the hens frightened them. The bulls were flighty and nervous. They had never been tied or rung, but they soon settled down.

That evening the Man filed away their "papers," their registration. He took a look at the papers for the biggest and oldest. Splendid Gaelic names: Gille Guidhe, Gille Bheag, Ossian of Glencaledon, Ridire Buidhe of Glenfalloch. Like reading poetry.

Two men from Graham River came overnight. They were heading down to the settlement with a string of pack-ponies. After turning them in the corral and forking hay to them, they lounged over to look at the bulls.

"Where in hell did you get them things?" they asked. "Look like big goats or somethin'. Don't say they's cattle?"

To which the Man replied dryly, "Well, I bought 'em for cattle—bulls, in fact. I'm going in for novelties, see? Beef isn't such a price." This made them change the subject, for ranchers don't like to stick their necks out. But they still looked puzzled.

It was just before Christmas. The Lad had been given a room in the house for the cold weather, so the bunkhouse was empty. The Graham River men took their bed-rolls there and started up the air-tight heater. The bunkhouse was rimmed with frost. They loosened up their eider downs, one on either side of the crackling stove. When supper was over, they smoked and chatted in the kitchen.

But they all jumped to their feet when the Woman, making coffee by the east window, suddenly called: "Fire!"

There was little they could do. The poplar logs and the brushwood supporting the sod roof of the bunkhouse were tinder dry.

Some saddles and harnesses in the lean-to at the north side were saved, the heat singeing the men's whiskers even as the cold winds cut their backs through their shirts, for no one had taken time to grab a coat.

The cabin and its contents were a total loss, rapidly disintegrating to a mass of hot, fluffy ashes. Air-tight heaters soon get red-hot if they are not checked in time, and cold eider downs have an eerie habit of opening up and creeping towards heat.

Next morning the Graham River men caught up their ponies and went down the trail at a trot, all their bells ringing in the frosty air. Little had been said. Hazards of the range country are accepted. If you didn't like them you went back to the hazards of the city—that was all.

Now, between the ordinary ranch chores, the men began cutting a set of logs for a new bunkhouse, fervently hoping they wouldn't have a fire in the big house before they completed the job.

One night, just before bedtime, the Lad went out. He burst in again, saying: "Come lookit them northern lights!" They all went out. They'd seen them often enough, but this was special. Over the roof-tree, in the centre of the star-spangled heavens, was the like of a great sunburst of rainbow hues. Beams flashed from it to every horizon.

They gazed in awe, the Lad craning his neck and exclaiming. The tall spruce by the barn stood etched in inky-black, every topmost twig outlined sharply against the silky, gently moving brightness, the high hump of Moose Ridge sharp as a knife-edge.

"The likeness of the glory of the Lord," murmured the Woman, thinking of Ezekiel.

Chapter 17

Spring was backward, hesitating, as it so often is. No juncos scratched among the dead leaves, no flickers yakked as yet. Only a pair of soft-voiced mountain bluebirds flitted from post to post, looking for some nook or cranny, for the nesting urge was upon them. The male, like an azure spirit, winged away and perched on a dead stub. His lady followed, popped into a broken-down woodpecker-hole and out again. Their search was over.

Of course the grey jays—the whisky-jacks—came even more often now. They already had mouths to feed, and if Small had no crust or bacon-rind for them they looked insulted and tapped at the east window. They had no fear of Kitty-Kotty. She was no match for the saucy clowns, although she had been known to feign sleep on the doorstep, only to leap high in the air and catch—as a boy catches a ball—a junco so foolish as to fly above her.

A bear had killed a cow not three hundred yards from the house. The dead beast lay on a cattle-trail behind some poplars, near the corner of the yard fence. The Man laid his plans. Dawn was the time for a bear to feed. The cow was too heavy for the bear to drag away as he would a calf. But shortly it would be dismembered, and then he would move it piece by piece into some inaccessible tangle.

The Man rose before daylight and pulled on a pair of soft moccasins. He would have to step noiselessly. The click of his rifle-lever would alert the bear, so at the house he loaded and cocked that weapon. You never got more than one chance.

Avoiding the west wind, he padded east and came in a circle, to drop behind a stump from where the carcass would be visible. Light was just drifting over the ridge. He waited, chilled to the bone. Now moving shadows tensed him. Once he half raised his weapon. The April bush was not yet leafing, and the poplar trunks, the willow-brakes, the ground, the sky—all were featureless, smoky grey. It was like looking into a deep pool or over a snowfield on a dull, colourless, shadowless day. Growing light—and silence—played strange tricks. Once there was a thud and a crackling, and he looked sharply to the left. It was only a red squirrel which had dropped to the ground and was cracking spruce cones. If it spotted him it would let out a warning, chattering like a busy-body, and that would end the hunt. But the squirrel did not see the grey, motionless man by the grey, motionless stump.

The sun came up, but no bear.

The Man was cold. Hungry too. He'd been there well over an hour. He would give it fifteen minutes. The sun rose higher, and he could see a plume of smoke above the treetops. The Woman was cooking breakfast. He rose, shivering. No bear today.

Next day was windless. The Man left the house a little later. Never repeat a pattern that fails, he thought, and made a cup of tea. With his stomach warmed, he set out, circling west this time, under cover of the bush bordering the meadow. In the stillness his moccasined tread made the hay-stubble crackle, and he was glad to crawl through the fence onto the soft dirt of the cow-trail. He followed the narrow path to where it turned east, and waited at the bend, now in view of the dead cow which lay a bare sixty yards away. Hardly had he stationed himself, hardly had he noticed an opening, a widening of the trail, where the bear was sure to cross, than that pale grey opening became dark. It was absolutely silent. The Man looked again. The dark patch moved forward towards the cow and stood, only its head moving, testing the still air.

Crack!

The sound of the shot shattered the dead silence, rumbling and rolling back to Round Hill.

The Man levered in another shell. He could see nothing. Had he shot at a mere shadow? Warily he stepped forward. No bear. No sign. Yes—no—yes. Cows didn't have three hind legs!

The bear, an enormous male, lay snuggled up by the off-side of the cow it had killed. "In death," said the Man solemnly, "they were not divided," and drew his skinning-knife. He was relaxed now, thinking: "The biggest son-of-a-bitch of a bear I ever shot—no wonder he was able to break that cow's neck. Pity too. She was a fine beast, and in calf."

"Laddie," the man called through the bunkhouse door, "something's raising hell. North. I'm away. Follow me up soon as you can."

The north valley was a blank. No cattle. At least, he couldn't hear or smell any. It was still too dark to see. But he had plainly heard from his bed a wolf howl, and then the bawling of what he thought must be a calf. The pea vine grew like alfalfa up High Springs Coulee. The pools were full too, and there should be cattle there this time of year. Old Fox—he *was* old now—snorted soon after he entered the timbered slope. It wasn't far to the spring. Then the Man smelt the beast-smell, the smell of a meat-eater. He heard something pad-pad. Something breathing hard, panting. A twig snapped, followed by dead silence.

Daylight was dimming the stars.

No cattle. No sound.

He rode south down the ridge, puzzled. All at once he came among them, bedded down above Moose Point. They showed no signs of being disturbed. Funny, he thought. Perhaps there was one cow alone up north. He rode back four miles, keeping on top, skirting the head of High Springs.

He heard a crash below him. He plunged down among the heavy scrub, branches whipping his face. He heard a loud blat to the right. This time it sounded like a yearling moose.

Crash, snap, thud, from below. Going downhill—west. Fainter each minute. The Man waited, heard nothing for ten minutes. Then, as daylight increased, he saw the Cow Moose working up the far side of the valley, up Wild Horse Ridge. A calf trotted at her side. He was sure the moose was being pursued, but no lean wolf-form appeared. He waited. The moose was now disappearing among the trees on top of the ridge.

Where was that yearling? Or had that blat to one side really been the calf? Whatever had attacked, bear or wolf, it had missed its breakfast.

He continued down the coulee. He wanted some coffee.

The moose, near the head of the coulee, heard the wolf pad-padding over the dead leaves. She was slaking her thirst at the pool below High Springs. It was dark under the overhanging willows and the overreaching boughs of tall spruce. A watery light glinted in the ripples from her lip.

Pad-pad. The sound was nearer. Her leggy yearling turned, blundering over a fallen log, his nostrils wide. The padding stopped. It was so silent that the thumping of the yearling's heart frightened him. Moving as quietly as only a moose can when she wishes, the cow drifted up the bank to where her calf lay. The yearling joined her. The calf, legs straddled, was now on its feet.

Pad-pad. From the right this time. To the left lay the cleft runnel of shallow water, beyond that a mass of deadfall spruce almost as high as a corral fence. Three pairs of eyes tried to pierce the gloom; three velvet noses twitched; three pairs of ears flicked back and forth.

Pad-pad again. Two yellow, hypnotic eyes appeared. And now the wolf-stench came, almost paralyzing the senses. The yellow eyes sank lower. The moose knew the charge was coming. Tearing her eyes and nose from what threatened to root her to the ground, she nudged her calf. They turned together, and with twin bounds were across the gulch. The cow reared to her full height, bringing her strong hooves down upon the half-rotten logs. The topmost broke, crumbled, and the cow fell to her knees, half rolling, half scrambling over. Blood was running from a gash in her leg. The calf at her flank floundered a moment, almost fell back. At that moment the Black Wolf charged for a quick grab at the calf's leg, but blatting with fear, the yearling blundered forward, striking the wolf—in mid-air—on the shoulder.

As the Black Wolf somersaulted, the yearling, his blood up now, reared, throwing all his weight behind his razor-sharp hooves. Had the blow told, the wolf would not have lived. But the yearling's feet slipped on the wet moss, and the wolf rolled aside and stood panting, blocking the way by which the cow had gone. The yearling blatted high and loud and fled into the spruce. He knew that he had to keep in the timber. In the open the wolf would have him. They both waited, the wolf panting, the yearling silent as death. Lost in the darkness of the bush.

For half an hour or more they played tag, hunter and hunted. The yearling had never been alone before. If he survived this, he would grow into a bull to be reckoned with. Now, he was scared. Where had his mother gone? Moose-scent still clung to the game-trail from the south, by which they had come. He began to follow it. He heard nothing. He hesitated, then circled east, rounded the head of the coulee. He paused again. Listened.

Now a faint sound came from the south, on the ridge. He blatted again. No reply. He made a half circle, avoiding the gulch. He couldn't go west—the wolf-smell was too strong. He flicked his ears this way and that. Daylight was coming.

Pad-pad. The wolf was moving again. Going north, working around behind him. He took a step, and another, in an agony of indecision.

Thud-thud-thud! Something coming from the top. Thud-thud. The cow? Her hooves in the soft duff and leaves? Past him, well south of the gully. The smell wasn't right. The yearling was puzzled. Should he follow, as all his life he had followed thumping hooves?

Pad-pad. Closer now. He saw a tall beast trotting below him. That decided him. The strange scent ahead was not so terrifying as the deadly sounds behind. He plunged to the right, following the hoof-beats, bent on catching up.

The Black Wolf, too, heard the thumps, and when the man-scent came to him he hesitated not a moment, but loped at full speed in the opposite direction.

The Man heard the hooves behind him.

"O.K., Laddie," he said over his shoulder. "Sorry I got you up. It was only a moose. I must have had the jitters."

No answer. Only the sound of a horse trotting closer.

"Say," the Man spoke again. "Got any makings? I'd like a

smoke." No answer. The Man turned and looked a yearling moose right in the eye.

The animal kept glancing back, crowding into Fox's rump, so that the old horse laid his ears back.

"That yearling must have been scared by a wolf—got separated from its ma," thought the Man. He'd known such things before. More than once he had, without intention, ridden close to moose calves, to have them get up and chase him. All they know is to lie still in the bush till mother's hooves come thumping up. If slowly, that meant take your time, get up, and have a drink. If fast, it was leap to your feet and follow, without any chit-chat. And he had been pressed once by a bull moose. At rutting time. All because he'd heard the old fellow in the bush and thought to tease him by imitating a cow moose on the run. He'd had to use the spurs that time, till the bull scented him and wheeled aside, grunting in anger. Moose don't see too well. For untold centuries before horses came the only hooved things which trotted in the bush had been other moose . . .

At the meadow-gate the yearling was still close behind. The Man had to shut the gate right in the puzzled animal's face. "Hope he don't break the fence down," the Man thought. But the moose didn't. When the Man last saw the yearling it was wandering west. Perhaps it could find its mother. Or perhaps calfhood was now behind it.

As he unsaddled Fox at the corral, the Man heard the Lad ride up from the east. Somehow, in the bush and the rough country, as yet hardly known to him, he had missed contact with his boss.

Chapter 18

The three-footed bitch had not pupped the previous summer. The strain of the spring before, the hard winter of crusted snow, all had indicated the need for a season's rest, and she had not conceived. But towards spring, in better flesh than for some years, she had again responded, and now a new litter was making her heavy. So it was that one evening she rose, stretched herself, looked hard at her mate, and started off up Moose Ridge, leaving the unlucky buttes behind. The Black Wolf followed, adjusting his lope to her slower, crippled one. This was she-business, and it was right that she should lead.

The Black Wolf's mate kept up a steady pace, and in two hours was circling the west side of the Big Burn. The burn stretched north and east for over two miles—a fearful scattering of black logs, most of them wind-felled, the few which still stood, pointing charred, maimed fingers towards the full moon which now appeared.

From the top of one of these a great owl, tufted like a lynx, hooted to his mate, who already fed her fierce-eyed owlets in the lofty nest of twigs among the spruce below.

Two mated foxes, a red and a silver-black, trotted cheek by jowl, slipping over the logs without a sound. They could hear another of their kind calling, calling from across the creek, from Wild Horse Ridge. Unmated, rejected, he barked in that *ha-ha-*

ha way which told its story. A snowshoe rabbit, snug beneath a charred log, froze lower at the sound, but in doing so caught a beam of moonlight on its big eyes—a mere sparkle but it was seen—and the two foxes jumped as one. They fed, ripping back the warm, tissue-thin skin. Already the little rabbits were assuming the colours of summer, and soon there were only tufts of fur, blue-white and brown, clinging to the reddened snow, now shrunk to small, watery patches on the shady sides of the logs.

Now the two wolves could be seen, black against the moonlit sky—big, powerful, panting a little like dogs. The foxes drifted through the shadows. They would not dispute hunting grounds with the larger animals. The fox still barked from the opposite ridge, but the wolves paid it no heed. The three-footed bitch had found what she wanted; the great, upturned root of a prostrate ancient spruce, which in falling had heaved up a mound of white clay.

The Black Wolf's wife looked hard, smelled hard, then turned to her husband. They touched noses briefly and set to work digging, he with both feet, she with one, making the dirt fly, snapping the rootlets of the wild raspberry canes and fireweed which had established themselves in the hard clay. The bitch was not well. Her nose was dry and feverish. Although now well-fleshed, she again felt the strain of the past two years. The moves, the crusted snow of winters, the long hunts, the invasion of the valley, the constant fear of traps—all these had weakened her, but she worked bravely on. The den finished, she rested, panting.

The Black Wolf pricked his ears and was gone in the predawn gloom. Then out of the stillness the bitch heard a thump, and another, and then a half howl, half whine—short, peremptory. She rose and followed. The Black Wolf had a buck by the flank and was striving to throw him down. The bitch leaped for the deer's throat, missed, and leaped again, only to be knocked sideways by a sharp front hoof which raked her ribs. But she had checked the buck, and her mate now brought its hind quarters down as she again moved in and seized its throat. She ate little. Her ribs hurt, as well as her footless leg, which had been her undoing.

Two days later her pups came—before their time, stillborn.

She scratched dirt over them, with the quiet acceptance of wild things.

The two wolves now abandoned the den they had newly dug, and thereafter laid up among the logs, rarely sleeping twice in the same spot. With no small mouths to feed, rabbits and mice were now enough for them, and they did not molest bigger stock that summer. Three strange bulls with hairy overcoats and long, wicked horns patrolled from July onward, and the wolves had no wish to dispute with them.

Again the Man felt and hoped that the wolves had moved away. Once, sure enough, as he rode over a patch of burnt clay he saw a fresh track and studied it, but it followed a straight course, as if the wolf had been travelling. He had heard of the one killed on the highway and another shot or trapped on Yellow Creek. Perhaps that had helped to discourage them.

But he was worried now as to why the cattle seemed to avoid the slopes of the Cutbank, where some of the best grasses on his range grew. While it was still "open" range, he had it all under grazing lease, as he did Moose Ridge and Burnt Creek as far as the buttes. He had gradually purchased most of the main valley, as well as the southern part of the Middle Fork and Wild Horse Creeks. The land had been offered at a low price, and the government agent had let it be known that a road was proposed which would make the area from Big Prairie north available to settlers. If you wanted to stay in the ranching game, you had best own your grass, he knew. He knew what settlers meant on a cattle range.

Musing on these things as he rode above the creek, he noticed three or four cows standing in a pool half a mile below. They were bunched up, looking at something. Their calves lay in the grass and scrub close to him, and the cows had evidently gone down to drink. All at once they started up the hill, tails coiled over their backs, breasting the steep water-trail at a trot.

"Bear!" thought the Man, and turned Fox downhill. The old horse was getting stiff. Soon he'd have to be pensioned. But he bravely ploughed his steep way down, making deep grooves in the sod.

The cows had reached the top by the time the Man hit the shallow pool in which they had been standing. His rifle was at the ready. It was very quiet, with the silence broken only by the twittering of the bank-swallows as they swooped in and out of their nesting holes in the high cutbank beyond. He looked and listened. Not a leaf stirred. He heard the cows bawl for their calves up above, and heard the answers.

Where there's a bear there had to be tracks, however, and he now stooped over the saddle-horn, scanning the sand and gravel to either side. Just below the pool he dismounted and squatted, rifle over knees. His hat pushed back, he stared at a track which was vaguely familiar. Something like a wolf's, but bigger, rounder, with no middle claw marks. His mind went back to a day in the Cariboo Country—how long ago?—and he knew what he was looking at. A big cat-track. A cougar's. Well, if a cougar from the mountains was making a hunting ground of Cutbank Creek, that explained a hell of a lot. For the first time he wished he had a dog, any old dog would take a cat-track and stick to it. He wondered where old Atchikoos was. Indian dogs would follow anything. He'd try to send word to Crying Girl Prairie, where Atchikoos lived, on the edge of cougar country.

That evening he told the Woman of the new menace.

"Well, I wasn't going to worry you," she replied, "but that night you were away looking for stock Small and I were frightened. Just after we went to bed we heard the most ghastly sound from down the creek—just west of the house. We thought it was a wolf or something, but it *was* scary."

"What d'you mean?" urged the Man. "A ghastly sound?"

"Well . . . like a woman *screaming*—or somebody being murdered—that's the only way I can describe it."

The Man spoke slowly. "Well, old girl, I guess that was it. A cougar, I mean. I've heard them, both in the Cariboo and the Chilcotin. Nothing else like it."

"What are you going to do about it?" the Woman asked.

"Try and get it, of course," he replied. "I'll send a note up to old Atchikoos. He can get Day Lily to read it for him. But good lord! How in hell can a fellow get on with his ranch work if he's got to spend half his time hunting?"

"You'll manage," said the Woman cheerfully.

They both went to the settlement that week. The Indian agent promised to get word to Atchikoos—he himself was taking a plane into the Indian village early next week, for it was treaty-payment time. "If that's soon enough," he had added. It was much sooner than he could get word by horseback, and the Man was well content.

That night they stayed with married friends, who expressed their sympathy with the Woman for her life in such a wild and forsaken country.

Surprised, the Woman replied. "Why—I'm having the best years of my life! The birds, the animals, the horses—I love them. And the mountains—they're never the same twice. And we have our books and our records and our radio—and lots of time to appreciate them. Why should you be sorry for me?"

Atchikoos came within a week. His squaw was with him, and a collection of rough, savage-looking dogs. These did not like the white-man smell and stayed close to their owners.

"Me camp?" the old Indian said, as he stood pigeon-toed by his buckskin.

Permission given, Atchikoos indicated to Old Mary a grove about a hundred yards away, where their camp would be delicately hidden from the house. When the tent was up, the couple tied their dogs to the trees. Soon the glow of their small fire died down, the light in the house went out, and the ranch slept.

By daylight next morning Atchikoos was mounted and away on his hunt. Two days went by before he returned. He came straight to the dooryard, where Old Mary sat chatting with the Woman and stroking Small's fair head with a brown and wrinkled hand.

Atchikoos threw down the tawny skin of the big cat with the gesture of a Don and uttered only one word—"Tobacco."

The Woman brought out a can of fine-cut, from which the Beaver deftly filled both his pipe and his empty buckskin pouch.

"Come." He spoke again, to his squaw. "Me eat now." And he led his tired horse away, while several bloody sacks, tied behind his saddle, swung with every step.

The Man rode in that evening, and on hearing the news went to the low, smoke-stained tent. Atchikoos told the story in broken English. "One day me ride, same place s'pose you tellum. No smell. Down creek dog he smellum mebbeso two mile." He

held up two fingers. "Cat he go big tree"—making a circle with his arms. "Dogs plenty yell. I come shootum, me. Ten dollar?"

"You bet ten dollars," replied the Man, delighted. The money changed hands.

Old Mary said, indicating a bubbling pot: "You eat? Plenty good!" The Man nodded, and the squaw fished out a piece of flesh as white as a chicken's. "Good!" she repeated, her old face cracking in a smile.

It *was* good. Sweet, with no animal flavour. He had eaten lynx in Saskatchewan's north. This was better, and again he thought: "All flesh is grass."

"You take house?" asked Mary. "Good for womans. Good for li'l papoose."

He declined. They might not care to eat a thing which made that ghastly noise in the night.

It was almost a week later that the Man found the heifer. Riding through a tangle of alders he stumbled on a curious mound from which Ted shrank and snorted. Dismounting, the Man investigated, pulling away withered branches mixed with scratched-up twigs, moss, and dead leaves, until he exposed a black shoulder, and finally the complete carcass of a fat two-year-old. Its neck had been bitten through, and part of the hindquarters and all the inward parts eaten.

This butchery was the cougar's work; no other animal, he knew, killed like this or buried its meat to ripen for future use.

Cougars kill at least once weekly—colts, cattle, or deer. But cattle were easiest, and by fall . . .

Atchikoos had made his hunt none too soon.

Chapter 19

The bulls were turned on the range in July. The cattle had increased to the point where they now grazed in three herds, so the big yellow one, Gille Guidhe, was driven south towards the buttes, the brindle across the creek towards the spruce swamp and Big Prairie, and the smaller dun up Wild Horse Creek.

The Man put out salt only on the west range, taking the blocks on a pack-horse. At the foot of the buttes was an alkali lick which provided mineral, while up the Wild Horse were the Salt Springs, all trampled and gouged by moose and deer, as well as cattle and wild horses. These spots and the watering places were the gathering grounds which at round-up time had to be thoroughly searched.

The yellow bull, bedded near his cows, was the first to his feet at the calf's terrified bawl.

The cattle lay in a small meadow a mile north of the buttes. All around were tall, thick-girthed poplars and shaggy spruces. The wind in their tops had deadened the sound of the bear's approach.

Now the bull roared long and loud, lifting his heavy bulk up from the matted grass. The whole herd followed suit, heaving from prone to knees, from knees to feet, each cow turning to its calf.

Again the calf bawled. It had left its mother's side to lie beside a cool log, and now saw the black shadow reared above it. One blow from the clawed pad, and the calf bawled no more.

With a mother's desperate courage the cow charged, but the bear easily evaded the attack and started to drag its prey away. Too late it saw the angry bull. It only felt a jarring sickening blow on its rump, and before it could turn, another and another.

With its back a flaming agony, the bear staggered to a tree, reached far up with its front limbs, and dug its claws deep in the soft poplar-bark. But just as it began the upward pull to safety the bull's hard forehead struck the killer in the middle of its back, completing the fracture, so that the bear's legs, now paralyzed, gave way, and it slipped down the trunk and crumpled to the ground. With a slashing sideswipe of his wide horns, the bull flung aside the upstretched arms of his enemy and knelt with his full weight on the heaving chest until the arched ribs suddenly cracked and the bear lay still. The cows, bunched tightly, never ceased from their high, angry bawling.

The Man heard it from where he rode down the trail, but by the time he reached the scene at a gallop, the job was done. The cows were trooping in single file towards the open country of the buttes, with the bull bringing up the rear, turning from time to time to paw dirt over his massive shoulders. His eyes were still red with anger under the shaggy forelocks cascading from his poll as he roared defiance in the direction of the lifeless black huddle at the foot of the scarred tree.

As the Man passed close, the still-maddened animal roared again and advanced on man and horse. Its head was covered in matted blood and dirt, dead leaves and twigs, and a flap of skin hung loose from its muzzle.

"There, old boy, it's only me!" said the Man in easy tones.

The bull wrinkled his nose at the scent which had meant hay and salt all winter. The red fire left his eyes, and his deep chest-rumblings ceased. He turned and trotted back to the moving herd, dodging the trees with his horn-sweep as a bull moose does.

The Man rode up to the bear and easily reconstructed the scene. Another calf lost—but the killer would kill no more.

Chapter 20

It was spring and the Man was counting his mares.

They were all there, Julie with a foal again. She was getting old, and this might be her last.

Both roans were heavy and would foal shortly.

The crooked-legged black; Susie, the wall-eyed cayuse he'd traded from an Indian on the Doig; these both had following foals.

The white-stockinged bay didn't look so good. He rode around her. Looked like she'd slipped her foal. Those damn drifts last winter. . . . Well, she'd soon flesh-up again.

The little buckskin pony-mare with the stripe down her back and the white pack-saddle marks—she'd foal any day.

As the mares stood in a little circle, blowing at him softly, ready to dash away, he ran his eyes over them. "Three up and three to go," he said aloud. "From seven—not so bad."

At his voice the mares shifted, and when Monte—the little black he was just breaking—tossed his head and pawed, they trooped off and scattered out to graze again.

Now for the following yearlings and two-year-olds. At this time of year they would graze a little apart from the mares but ready to join up if anything scared them.

The Man could see some backs moving above the willow brush, and rode around. The young horses trotted into the open and greeted Monte, who until last year had run with them.

There should be three two-year-olds, a colt and two fillies. And six yearlings. Nine altogether. He could only count seven.

He checked again, riding the bush in a circle. He found nothing. The two fillies were missing. They would never leave the bunch, he knew.

He circled again, casting wider and wider until he found himself on Wild Horse Ridge.

A mile from the mares, on the main game-trail to the north, he found tracks—plenty of tracks. A bunch had trotted in single file down the ridge from the north.

Again suspicion blackened the Man's mind. Back there, over twenty miles, were the horse traders' corrals and camp. Had *they* taken the bunch north, cut out the fillies, and chased the rest back to their range? It wouldn't take more than a night to run them up, no more than half a day for the mares to work back.

His first impulse was to back-track the horses and tackle those shifty fellows. But second thoughts told him this would avail little. The fillies would probably be way back in a hidden corral he'd never find; or even hobbled in some bush meadow. Sure as the devil they'd have a dog, or dogs, which would give the alarm long before he got there.

You just can't accuse people without real evidence. Whatever the picture might be they'd have a glib story—probably say they'd done him a good turn by chasing his mares back—they weren't responsible how many, hazards of the range, etc.—and make *him* feel in their debt. "Shore," they'd say, grinning up their sleeves, "too bad. Why not take a look around here? We'll shore look out for them fillies of yourn and let you know."

Even if he found the fillies in their corral, it would be: "We wuz just going to saddle up and let you know. Somebody's been a-chasing them, but we ran 'em in our corral, etc., etc."

He knew they wouldn't try to sell the fillies—not with that LADDER S brand on them. They'd simply range-break them, turn a stud out, and there'd be a colt to brand each year after weaning. Probably feed the colts in a corral till they got over following their mothers—turn 'em loose later. Even if they did go back to following—family ties are strong with horses—what could anyone prove? A yearling might follow any old mare, so far as the Law was concerned.

In the Old Days it had been different. Two or three ranchers' words were apt to be enough. Not now. The Man had seen court cases before. He knew that what looked open-and-shut to a stockman meant nothing to smart lawyers. Like family resemblances, for instance. A rancher knew what old mare was grandmother to a certain filly simply by comparing profiles, nature, gait, and sometimes markings.

"That there mare had a pear-shaped spot of white inside the left hind leg," he had heard a rancher say from the witness stand.

"So what?" the defence lawyer had snapped. "So might I." The court had laughed, and the rancher, red-faced, had shut his mouth.

The judge was always liable to dismiss cases for want of evidence, and add in stinging tones: "It's up to you stockmen to watch your property and not keep bothering the Law!"

As if a rancher *didn't.* And they never understood that on open range property rights had to be safeguarded by custom—which, the Man reflected, is after all the basis of Law.

His only hope was to wait, to try and locate the fillies on the traders' range, cut them out or rope them, and bring them home; saying nothing. A row would only do harm. He knew these types. He knew how they had run stock, crippled stock, and cut fences, in pure revenge—down South.

Anyway, those tracks explained the mare slipping her foal. She had been chased hard—likely she'd had a fall or got overheated.

Nevertheless, the next time he went to the settlement he had a talk with the Mounted Police corporal.

"Not much I can do, really—not at this stage," the corporal said. "We've only lately taken over from the Provincials, and we're short of men. With the oil boom starting and scads of new people coming in, our hands are full. We've had two murders already this year, and there's a rash of petty theft. Also, none of my young fellows could ride five miles without getting sore bums. Wish I could make a patrol myself. I'd love a few days in the saddle—but I simply can't. The old man would raise the dickens. Times have changed, old boy. We don't have time to prevent—we just take action after. Do the best you can, and we'll try to check any trucks taking horses to the Yukon. Try to catch 'em at it, and call on us if you get a real case."

"Thanks," the Man said, and left. He was thinking what a slim chance there'd be of "catching" anyone. The traders went in twos—one man to two would make a laughing-stock of you in court. And the ranch work had to go on.

Back home there was land to break, hay to put up, a binder to bring in (that alone would take a week on the trail for him and the Lad and four horses). *He* couldn't afford to ride by night as those guys did!

As the summer waned, the incident lost some of its sting. After all, suspicion might have put him on the wrong track. Those fillies might turn up. Maybe wolves. . . . But he'd seen no circling ravens, heard no wolves or coyotes, smelt nothing on his rides.

He had to admit there were a thousand hazards on the range—cutbanks could slide, lightning could strike, loco-weed and larkspur were poisonous. . . . But why two fillies? Why not geldings, colts, mares? Geldings, branded, weren't salable; they didn't reproduce. Colts had to be altered. Old mares were clever at dodging for home. He had come full circle.

He'd just have to bide his time.

Chapter 21

The new binder finally came up the trail, half-dismantled and chained down to a plank wagon bed. The oats were cut, stooked, and stacked. A heavy crop.

Another winter came, ushered in by a late November snowstorm, as the weetigos of Keewadin plucked their white geese.

One evening, when the family sat around the big heater, the Lad, normally not given to talk, said: "Them beaver got two more dams on the Cutbank, one on Wild Horse, and three-four on the Middle Fork. They've got the ford plugged on Cutbank, and it'll be hard to cross come spring. Reckon we should trap some afore we get the seed grain."

The Man said: "Well, we won't need to cross there for a bit. Early spring's the time to trap beaver. Say—how'd you like to trap some, eh? And there's a few mink up Wild Horse, plenty of foxes, and always the chance of a lynx—saw one at the buttes last winter. Course, if I give you permission to trap on the whole ranch—that's about fifteen thousand acres, lease and all—*I* should get something out of it, eh?"

The Lad grinned. "Say, would you? I mean, I get a few hours free when I'm feeding stock. And I could watch my beaver-traps along the creek when I'm riding at calving time. I mean—could I?—Would you?"

"O.K.," replied the Man. "You get good wages—eh? So if you

trap on my time you'll give me—let's see—say 30 per cent. I'll supply the traps."

"It's a deal!" cried the Lad.

"Only, remember," the Man went on, "no more than two beaver from each dam—except the ones at the fords. We may have to clean them right out or we won't be able to get around or bring the seed grain across. And *no* snares. I don't want stock crippled. And I don't want everything, even foxes, cleaned right out. See?"

"You bet," said the Lad emphatically. "I'll remember. And next time you're in town can you get me about a dozen No. 1 Victor Jump traps, about the same of No. 2s, and a few bigger ones? I can use the .22 rifle for squirrels—they're worth thirty-five cents each now—mink will fetch fifteen to twenty dollars, and if I get a lynx . . . I'll set the small traps for weasel and mink now; later for muskrats. The bigger ones I'll use up in the valley in the big spruce-run—might get a lynx. And for fox I'll have sets on the ridge. As soon as there's open water in the spring I'll set for beaver on the creeks! I'll have to wait for more snow before I'll find enough sign to know where to set for mink and weasel . . . oh boy!"

The Lad did well with his trapping. By Christmas he had two red and one cross-fox—the latter a beautiful creature with its mixture of red and grey hairs, dark across the shoulders and down the back. To everyone's surprise he also caught a fisher—a pecan-fisher, which is the largest of the weasel clan, almost as big as a fox. This was in the heavy spruce near the Salt Springs, and the same area yielded several marten.

The young trapper rose early and started hauling feed to the wintering bunch at daybreak, while the Man did the barn chores and forked hay to the sixty-odd calves in the weaning corral. He was proud of these cross-breds. They were growthy rascals, as his old rancher friend had predicted.

The bulls had their own corral of heavy logs. As he fed them he reflected that they had grown and filled out enormously. The yellow one must have horns all of three feet long—good for protecting the cows!

Every day at noon the Lad returned from his work, and if there was no wood to haul from the bush that day he would be off to his trap line after dinner, sometimes on snowshoes, sometimes on horseback, according to the terrain. After supper his light would glow from the bunkhouse as he sat down to skin the day's catch. The greater number would be squirrels and weasels, now white ermine. Even the squirrels were worth thirty-five cents apiece, and the woods were full of them. The fleas which jumped from these little animals he accepted with philosophy and Keating's powder.

With so few traps, compared to the vast size of his line, he would do little damage to the fur-bearers, and they would be in no danger of serious reduction in numbers.

As the sun began to rise earlier and the willow-bark began to take on the richer hue of spring, the Black Wolf's mate again made a decision. She hated the place where her pups lay mummified in the dry clay.

The wind from the west was roaring over the ridge and the smell of spring was strong in the air when the two wolves set out, following Wild Horse Creek southwards. They threaded their way among the fringing willows which covered the shallow banks and which sometimes met above the deeply worn channels. Where the creek turned west, around the shoulder below Wild Horse Point, began the deep canyon which no stock penetrated or crossed; narrow, twisting, and gloomy, half-choked with fallen trees and obstructed by great rocks between which, when the ice melted, the freed waters would gurgle and fret.

The wolves came to an old spruce which had shot upward from these dark depths in search of the sun till its crest had topped the canyon wall. The bitch stopped and looked at the tree's base, but passed on, as the Black Wolf caught up to her. Together they kept on to the junction beyond the gash, where Middle Fork came in from the north on the west side of the ridge. They crossed over the softening ice, already an inch deep in water from the chinook, exploring, seeking, snuffing here, poking there. The bitch sat down. The Black Wolf, with a leap, pinned down a ruffed grouse which had sat in the snow, frozen at their approach, its crop full of desiccated high-bush cranberries.

The two wolves shared the warm meat. Licking their lips, they rose. The bitch looked back over her shoulder and whined softly. Her mate pricked his ears. They both turned and trotted back without a pause to the canyon. Under the gnarled, crooked roots of the big spruce they stopped and together began to dig. No one could see the den-mouth unless they went on their knees in the stream bed—if indeed anyone had reason to clamber down into such a deep and forbidding place. It was barely above high-water mark and sloped upward for several feet before it levelled out. No water could flood it.

To the north, following the curve of the bend, stood a high knoll, just below Wild Horse Point itself but separated from that open butte by heavy poplar woods. This overlooked the creek in both directions, and from it the Black Wolf could also see across the meadow to the whitewashed house of logs where the Man lived. This spot became the wolf's lookout. There was no more than half a mile between his lying-up place and the jumble of corrals and buildings, and now as he lay there he could see the Woman hanging out washing and hear the bulls rubbing on the corral-rails to ease the itchiness of spring.

The creek had run in full flood and was now subsiding, although it was still fed to a good depth by the melting snows of the high country. The Lad had set his beaver traps. At Thunder Creek ford he caught five beavers and released the pent-up waters of the dam by breaking down the sticks and trash in the centre. The trickle below the dam became a flood, and soon the dam was lowered enough to allow the ford to be used again.

Between visits to his traps he kept an eye on the calving cows from Moose Point to the buttes.

Now he changed places with the Man, who took over the riding of the south cattle, to allow him to try his traps on the Wild Horse. Three nights later he had taken four beavers there and opened up the dam which hindered the cattle from crossing. When he returned with his skins he had something to tell.

"You know," he said, "there's wolves around here again. I skinned out a couple of beaver below the ford yesterday. Today the bodies have gone, eaten up clean except for a couple of front paws. It was wolves. I seen a track."

"Which way were the tracks heading? Could you tell?" asked the Man quickly.

"I finally lost the tracks, but they seemed to be leading off to the ground-birch flat west of the ridge. I got a couple more beaver on the Middle Fork, and maybe he smelt them," was the reply, as the Lad rolled a smoke thoughtfully.

"Could be a travelling wolf," his boss conjectured. "When I trapped beaver back on the prairies I often had a coyote follow me up for the left-overs, and I've known a timber wolf do the same in the North. No doubt he'll move on."

Nevertheless the Man rode up to see the tracks for himself, but the creek had risen again after a night of rain and he could make little of them.

Two weeks later the men hit the trail with two wagons to bring in the seed grain. It would take a hundred bushels to sow the new breaking. All the older land—over a hundred acres—was now in brome grass, promising a heavy crop of hay.

The Lad took his winter's fur catch with him. Eleven beavers, with the foxes, martens, ermine, and squirrels, as well as several coyotes and the precious fisher. The Hudson's Bay fur-buyer gave him his cheque, which he promptly cashed at the bank.

When he paid out the Man's share, the latter exclaimed: "What are you going to do with all that money?"

The Lad hesitated. "Well," he said at last, "if they can run with yours I'd like to get a couple of cows. I know a fellow has two for sale—pretty good Herefords. Going cheap. Not now, of course. In the fall when he weans the calves. It's my brother down at Beaverlodge. He says he'll truck them as far as the stopping house, and I thought maybe we could bring them up with the pack-ponies after we drive the beef down."

"You've got a head," said the Man. "We'll do just that—they'll make money for you. And I tell you what. You know that late heifer calf—the little 'un? I'll give her to you. She isn't branded yet. You'd best register a brand, and we'll slap that on her as well as on your two. Then when you're ready to take some land you'll have a bunch started."

"Say, thanks a lot!" And the Lad grinned in the happy way he had.

They had to buy sacks for the oats, as usual. It seemed that no matter how many they got each spring, by the end of the year they were either leaky or had been used for other purposes or else seemed to have just disappeared! This meant stopping in the settlement, and they noticed how the place was growing. A new hotel was going up to replace the old log one, and a new post office and a service station. But old Mark, the Chinese café owner, was just the same.

"I don't see for long time," he grumbled. "Why you stay that damn bush all-time?" And as they paid for their lunch he handed out a bag of oranges. "For li'l girl," he said.

The return trip was the usual slow affair, doubling up on both down and uphill grades, the horses tired and sweating by the time they camped at Thunder Creek. It was hot and dusty, forecasting a dry summer, and already the young grass of the sidehills was starting to burn to brown before it was two inches high.

But it began to rain next morning. A drizzle at first, what the Man called a Scotch mist, obscuring the hills, but before they reached Burnt Creek it became a downpour, and they found the short but steep crossing as slippery as grease. The second wagon slipped sideways, away from the gradual bank at the ford, and it stopped with a jar, with its front wheels against the steep bank below the ford.

Slipping and sliding in the mud and knee-deep water, the Man and the Lad unloaded the heavy bags, covering them with a tarp on the sodden bank above. They unhooked the wet, dispirited horses, and with a chain to the axle dragged the front wheels of the wagon back to the ford and so up safely on top. Loaded up again and on the trail, the wagons groaned on the soft ground, while water streamed from the horses' flanks and the hat-brims of the drivers. The Man had tried to roll a cigarette in the lee of a wagon but hadn't been able to keep his fingers dry and had finally tossed the saturated paper and tobacco from him with a curse.

It was altogether a sorry outfit that arrived at dark and squelched to the bunkhouse, where the grain would be stored till the ground dried sufficiently for sowing.

As they pulled the harness from the tired animals the Man said: "Feed 'em up for the night. Give 'em plenty. . . . And, say, we won't unload those bags to-night. The grain will be

O.K. under the tarps. We'll go eat. All we'll do after supper is —you get your wood and water, and I'll milk the cow."

Time passes quickly in the busy season, and soon the crop was well up and in the shot-blade. The hay-flat shone under a hot summer sky, the tall grass, already purplish-red with feathery, blossoming heads, rippling under the marching cloud shadows.

It was Sunday. Everything was ready for haying. The Man hoped the weather would hold. He glanced at the two mowers. They were freshly oiled and greased, their knives sharpened and their bent guards replaced.

The work-teams were ready in the corral—Mae, the big grey, and her mate Barney; Nancy and Lady, the bay mares. The brood-mares had been turned out west of the hayfield. The grass was good on the slopes which fell away to the creek, the far side of which was so rugged and heavily wooded that there was little to tempt the animals to cross. Nor would they be likely to work north, for the short distance between the meadow fence and the canyon had been blocked by rails.

From where the Man now sat on the banking of the house, on the shady side by the water barrels, he could see the grazing mares with their foals. He had borrowed a well-bred stallion last summer from the man at Graham River, who had been only too glad to rid himself of the sense of "being beholden" because of the matter of the bunkhouse fire. The foals—fine-boned, leggy —were the result. They should all make good saddle-stock.

The one from Susie, the Indian pony, might be a little small, but it would be a fine mount for a woman or a big child when it had its growth. It had inherited its mother's wall-eye and widely blazed face, as well as a spot or two of white on its flanks—a heritage from a pinto grandmother.

"Dinner!" called the Woman, and the Man rose, stubbing out his cigarette. A day's rest felt good. On Sundays he shaved, donned clean clothes, and took it easy, no matter the urgency of the work. Man and beast needed that day. Work must not be the end-all, or you got bushed. At mid-morning the Prayer Book came out, and after that there was time to stroll or sit, look or think—to enjoy the rolling hills, the clumps of trees, the waving hay, the distant blue mountains. Life was good.

That afternoon they decided to have a ride. Small could now sit gentle Robin with ease and had her own child's saddle. They would go away up the Porcupine Trail and see if the saskatoons were yet ripening. The Lad promised to watch the roast between spells of reading.

The saskatoons were just beginning to show a flush of red. It would not be long now before they would be baking saskatoon pies, and perhaps they would make a little wine for Christmas.

Coming back through the scattered poplars, the rays of the low sun made the shade-loving wildflowers even brighter. Acres of Indian paintbrush made a carpet of salmon-red on the lower slopes, dotted here and there by clumps of larskpur, richly blue and nodding on five-foot stalks.

The little party watched a doe with twin spotted fawns slip cleverly under the lower wire of the fence separating the wrangle field from the open range.

As they approached the pale blur of the house the nighthawks were zooming overhead in pursuit of winged insects. Once a low-quartering owl swooped down over the little grey cat and frightened her so that she fluffed her tail and sprang to the back of Small's saddle. Kitty loved to follow saddle-horses so long as it was a really short ride and so long as the horse did not race along. Robin was used to her, for she slept on that pony's back in winter, when at bedtime the Man carried her to the barn for the night.

In the morning, as soon as the Man entered the stable, she always raced for the house, and by standing on her hind legs could pull down the latch-string, and by the weight of her body open the kitchen door. From there she raced about the house (her house, she thought it was) on a tour of inspection.

Poor Kitty! She was destined, like Lillian, to be a maiden cat all her life—for there was not a tom within miles!

The party unsaddled in the deepening dusk and strolled slowly to the house. It was too fine a night to hurry, and they lingered on the path, talking quietly and looking upward at the stars as they came out one by one. Most prominent at first was the Plough, or as they called it, the Wain, and they followed its pointers to the pin-prick of light which was the North Star. The evening star was setting and already looked red. And then gradually the Milky Way began to show. The Man told how often he had guided himself by its south-west direction, when the North Star was obscured by clouds. It was very still, yet the whole world seemed to vibrate and breathe like a living thing—but very softly. There came a cool gust of night wind, and Small shivered a little. With one accord they all entered the log building. The Woman lit the oil lamps so they might read a little before bed-time.

Chapter 22

Next day the peaceful hayfield rang to the clatter of the mowers. It was good to sit on the moving machine, good to see the heavy swathe fall, good to guide the fast-stepping horses, to feel them tug on the lines. It was work to take a pride in.

The Lad was doing well with the bays on the lead mower. He could turn a neat, square corner, now he had got the knack of backing the off-horse a little as he lifted the cutting-bar with its foot lever.

As each round took them to the west fence the Man became more and more puzzled. Why was the wall-eyed pony by herself in the same spot where he had seen the bunch yesterday—near the canyon? And why did she graze in a small circle and keep stopping to look about? She should have been with the rest. It was hot, the kind of day when horses would want to stand in the shade of the bush, heads over their neighbours' necks. Then why wasn't Susie with them? He couldn't see her foal either. At first he thought it must be lying down nearby, but as the day wore on he watched in vain for it to run to its mother for refreshment. Something was wrong. A grazing mare, if she does raise her head, looks only in one direction—towards where her foal lies. Not here, there, and everywhere. Mares aren't like cows. If they go to drink, they don't leave their foals for hours in the grass. They always have them at foot. And foals never lie for long, but must be up to gambol and play around their dams.

By supper-time thirty acres of hay lay in swathes, making a neat pattern on the valley floor. Tomorrow, if it wasn't too cloudy, it would be ready to rake.

After supper the Man said: "Lad, you fix the horses for the night and milk Heather, will you? I'm going for a little ride."

As he dismounted and led his horse through the wire gate onto the west range, the wall-eyed mare whinnied and trotted up, touching noses with Ted.

Ted was now the Man's top horse, for he had been obliged to pension off old Fox, who, by the looks of him, might not last another winter.

He wished he had Fox today. Ted had not yet a tithe of the old horse's wisdom. If something was wrong, if something was dead, Fox would know—and given his head, was better than any man.

The mare still talked to Ted, and before mounting, the Man looked quickly under her belly; her bag was full, the teats unsucked and dry. Something had happened to Susie's foal.

Mounting now, the Man rode to where the mare had grazed all day. The grass was long, spotted with creamy white bedstraw all in blossom, trampled and laid down in spots; but this did not differ from the beds a troop of mares always left behind them. Now he began to ride in a widening circle, the wall-eyed mare following anxiously, trustingly. Look as he might he saw no dead foal, no spot of blood, no sign of a struggle.

He flushed a hermit thrush from her nest in a tangle of fallen trees at the edge of the prairie glade, noticed that the squirrels were already gathering the July mushrooms from among the long grass and already had a willow bush crammed with them, the round, domed fungi wedged among the upper twigs to dry for winter. He heard the sharp "peenk" of a sapsucker and saw the little patterns of holes bored in the bark of an alder. The setting sun was still hot, the bees still droned in the bedstraw, and the thrush slipped back to her nest.

Then he struck the track of the mares where they had wound their way through the lush growth of mid-summer, heading for the water-trail which snaked down the steep, choppy hills to the creek.

As he started over the brow, where the ancient trail was deep worn, dry and dusty, he could tell that the mares had been travelling at the high trot. This was not unusual in fly-time, but still, an easier gait would have seemed more in keeping with a path so steep and winding.

The wall-eyed mare still followed, and he realized how thirsty she must be after her all-day vigil in the heat. The minute they came to the creek she waded belly-deep and buried her nose in the cool, rushing stream.

He found the mares almost a mile south. They nearly jumped out of their skins as he came suddenly around a small spruce clump onto the flower-spangled prairie through which the creek flowed at this point. They gathered, foals at flanks, and blew noisily at his approach.

"They're spooky again," the Man thought. "They've been frightened. It couldn't have been a bear—they make a hell of a mess dragging things about. And I doubt there's another cougar around. Must be a wolf—but how the dickens could it kill and eat a foal and leave neither blood nor drag-marks? And they don't eat the big bones or the skull. Funny."

Puzzled, he turned back. The sun was setting, the night vapours already rising from the creek. No use to look there. If the foal had somehow drowned, the mare would not have been up on the bench all day.

There was a big day's work ahead for the morrow. He needed sleep. There was nothing more he could do now. It was ten o'clock, but in this latitude—five hundred miles north of the border—it was not really dark till eleven. As he started up the water-trail he realized that the bereaved mare was still pressing hard on Ted's heels.

Funny, he mused, funny how all these animals trusted him. They thought he could perform miracles. It made him remember the long-ago years when he had herded sheep in Alberta. The lambs would lie in the mouth of a badger burrow when the sun was hot on the plains. There they would go to sleep in the shade, on the cool earth, and gradually slip farther and farther down until there was no room for them to scramble to their feet. And there they died if they were not rescued. But the ewe always came to where he sat on a rock, crook in hand, and she would stamp her foot and bleat, turning her head to show him. And he would rise and say: "All right, old mother," and go to the rescue, the ewe leading the way with mincing steps.

He took a last long look over the rim of Wild Horse Canyon. It was gloomy down there. He could hear the tinkle of the current below but could see nothing. He rode home and shut the gate in the poor wall-eye's face.

Haying went well, for the good weather held. Stacks began to loom up on the meadow, two at the far end, one topped and one half-built just west of the house. They'd finish it today, the Man thought, as he lit the stove and set the kettle to boil for early tea. He rapped on the bunkhouse door, called: "Ten minutes after five!" and heard the Lad's sleepy answer.

As he came back from feeding the horses, the Man stood for a moment, looking at the weather. There were a few clouds in the south-west but nothing to worry about. The plovers on the flat were silent. Another good day ahead, he guessed, and a hot one.

Something caught his eye on the hayfield, just beyond the yard fence; something black. A yearling steer? How come a yearling in the field, and the cattle miles away?

Then all at once, he came fully awake.

It was the Black Wolf! The wolf he thought had died or left the country. Walking calmly towards him, facing the early rays of the sun, which now streamed over the hilltop.

Quietly, not taking his eyes from the animal, he edged to the door, which faced east. He could hear the Woman setting down the tea-caddy. Quietly still, he pulled the leather latch-string, pushed the door gently open. The Woman looked up, ready to speak.

"Quiet!" said the Man in low tones. "My rifle."

She took the Winchester from its nail and handed it to him without a word. For a brief moment, as he grasped the weapon and cocked it, he took his eyes off the wolf, and when he raised them and his rifle the brute was running full out, just disappearing behind the stacks. The Man ran to one side, but when

he saw the wolf again it was out of effective range and just entering a patch of willows. Panting, the Man returned, but not before he had investigated the haystacks.

"What was it?" asked the Woman. "I ran to the west window, but all I could see was you rushing like a madman around the haystacks!"

"That damn wolf," he replied. "Imagine! It had been sleeping on the haystack—that unfinished one. I saw the dent of its bed and the scattering of hay where it jumped up. I know that's a favourite sleeping place for a coyote—but a timber wolf! That close to the house. And I thought there wasn't one for miles. But I'm sure it's the same old black devil! Probably sleeping off a big load, like they do. Made him sleepy. . . . Why! I'll bet that's the beast took old Susie's foal. If only I'd had my rifle right there!"

"Good gracious!" said the Woman. "What about Small? I mean . . . I can't let her go beyond the fence if that animal is about. Bears are bad enough—but a wolf! You'll simply have to do something about it! I know you keep telling me that wolves won't attack humans, but there's always a first time, and I don't trust them. Small isn't a man! And what about Red Riding Hood? Don't laugh—I'm really scared. I shan't sleep at night if this goes on. Every time I hear a cow bawl I wake up!"

"Sure, I'll do what I can." The Man sounded worried. "But one wolf doesn't make a pack, and he could be denned up miles away. But I sure don't want you scared—you never have been before."

"Perhaps not, but this is *too* close," she replied. "Why don't you carry that rifle *all* the time? If, as you say, wolves know so much, that might at least keep them at a distance.

"Or get a gun you could carry in your hip pocket, instead of that old spotted handkerchief," she went on; but seeing the look of concern on the Man's tired face, quickly changed the subject and added: "which, by the way, is filthy! Get a clean one from the drawer, and relax and eat your breakfast.

"You've got a big day ahead—I'll look out for Small."

To himself the Man thought: "This is it. No matter how I feel about it, I'll use poison the first chance I get. Can't have her worried like that, and I suppose this life is kind of frightening to a woman—even one as brave as her."

Chapter 23

Wolves actually did not cause as much personal worry to the Woman as many less savage-looking creatures. The loss of a two-dollar hen was more her tragedy than was the killing of a sixty-dollar calf or an even more valuable steer. She did not care much about money. A subsistence living was quite enough, she thought, and keeping out of debt a main concern.

Anyway, cattle—except for Heather, the milk cow—were not intimate friends. Heather was always safe in her own little pasture, and she disdained to try to join the rough, rude range cattle. And her calf was always in the barn, pail-fed. If anything happened to *it,* now, that would indeed be tragic; you couldn't give your fingers to be sucked every day without loving the little, bunting beast.

And the hens, of course, were all old friends, with proper names. "My Black Hen" (which laid eggs for gentlemen) couldn't be spared. Nor Speckledy Hen, who laid in the house. Nor Charlotte, nor Mrs. Buff-Orpington, nor Crosspatch . . . not old Crosspatch, even . . .

But when the goshawks found that chickens were always in the same place, and therefore easier to hunt than rabbits or wild prairie hens which might be anywhere, the big, cloudy-grey birds began to make more and more frequent visits; so the Woman learnt to aim a .22 rifle—but these hawks were elusive and knew how to approach under cover of the trees. You never knew when one was sitting, silent and perfectly still, among the twigs and leaves. The first hawk the Woman shot was a triumph, and she got the Man to hang it in full view to discourage other hawks—for she could not bring herself to touch the big bird with its red eyes, cruel hooked bill, and strong, yellow, taloned feet.

She had to admit that this scarecrow did not help much, for the very next day another goshawk—a cross-barred hen bird—took poor Charlotte from under her nose.

It was the smaller sharp-shinned hawks which often tried for the young chicks, but Speckledy and Mrs. Buff-Orpington usually put them to flight, with some help from the silver rooster; but he was not the bird he had been since a fox nearly caught him in the nettles and gave him such a fright that he crept into a haystack and stayed there for nearly two days. The Man said the fox *had* got the old fellow, since he had run out just in time to see some sickle-curved tail feathers floating on the wind, but later the Woman, searching the stacks for stolen nests, pulled Chanticleer from his hiding place. He scraped a wing in thanks, and "tup-tupped," which made her laugh and say: "You old humbug, you!"

She didn't mind weasels. They were friendly little chaps. The Man had a pet one in the barn, which used to drink from a saucer of milk. She had heard him say that in the North almost every trapper had one at his cabin. They kept down the mice and were good company.

Pack-rats—now they were something different. Nasty, smelly things, all furry and soft. They crept around like Kipling's Chuchundra, afraid to get out in the centre of a shed or room. If you hit one with a club it went all *flat*—as if it had no proper bones. And their big, black, sad-looking eyes . . .

One summer's day she climbed into the barn-loft, because the hay-door was open and she thought one of the Dawn Sisters might be laying there—it cackled every morning from that direction. What a stench! Under the hay she could hear something burrowing about and *thumping*. Pack-rats in a barn were awful! They fouled the hay so the horses wouldn't eat it. But worse still, they chewed the strings off saddles and ruined harnesses, liking the taste of Neat's foot oil. When the Man came to supper she told him. He figured the animal must have a nest under the hay—but, good lord! This was the busy season, and it would take hours to shift the hay and find it!

Next day he needed new bolts and slats for the hay-loader, which had picked up a couple of snaggy roots, breaking three cross-slats. He kept the bolts in an open box in the hay-loft, where it was dry. The box was there, and a few bolts and slat-irons, all covered up with balls of dry horse dung. But it had been full of bolts! One more break-down, he thought, and he would *have* to move that darn hay.

He knew pack-rats—trade-rats some people called them. Those furry, squirrel-like rodents were honest in their way. They would always make a trade for whatever they took. Why, he remembered how in the Chilcotin they had once filched from him more than half a ten-pound box of prunes, meticulously replacing them with pine cones. He knew they loved shiny, metal things, and he shouldn't have left the box of bolts there.

So for the time being he set a trap near the hay and baited it with a piece of paper from a chocolate box the Woman had kept since Christmas for the reason that it had primroses on it. He caught the pack-rat. A female with big nipples, and he could not help admiring the fine, silvery fur. He reset the trap, but the other rat was either forewarned or had left.

When he did find time to remove the hay, the Man uncovered the nest. It was a yard square, made of hay, green twigs with leaves on, bark stripped from the corral-rails, hair from grooming the horses, and chicken-feathers. It smelt like a sewer. But within it were his missing bolts, still shiny, and a jack-knife somebody had lost long before. And seven little wizened corpses, pink-footed and dry. Baby rats, they were, starved for lack of milk. It's a brutal life, thought the Man, as he so often did. Survival of the fittest meant you were always killing things. Well, the blessed rats should have stayed in the stinking tunnels and fissures of the rim-rock a mile away; that was where they were intended to breed unmolested, with only spruce cones and bits of glittering quartz to play with.

The Woman finally caught the fat male pack-rat in the kitchen. How it got there they had no idea, but there it was, running—or rather sliding—in that creepy, silent way they have, along a beam. She picked up a piece of stove-wood and tried for five minutes to summon up the courage to hit it. Then all at once the animal dropped to the floor with a dull, pack-rat *thump!* and disappeared behind the Dutch dresser. She tried brooms, pokers, anything, while Small sat on the table and looked on. It *wouldn't* come out, and it smelt scandalous.

So she got the trap and set it as the Man had told her, baiting it with a shiny button, pushing it between the dresser and the wall, where the wretch would have to come out. And when the trap snapped, what with the scuffling and thumping, you would have thought she had caught a tomcat at least. That is what she told the Man, and went on to say she had drowned it in the swill-pail, holding it down with her stove-wood club, and it hadn't shown the least fight! She swore that if any more pack-rats came around, she would leave them to him to tackle. They were such horrible creatures; yet pretty, in a way . . .

He knew she had been upset, and didn't blame her.

"Why don't you let me saddle Ted for you—or Monte? He's gentle-broke now. You could take a ride by the buttes and visit the new woman at Yellow Creek, eh? Stay all day. The child will be O.K. We'll be fencing the stacks and we'll watch her. Why don't you?" he urged.

"Well, I might, tomorrow—it's too late today," she replied dubiously. "But give me Ted. I've no faith in your 'gentle-broke' Monte. I see when you start to mount—he's away like the wind. And I like a horse that at least pretends to stand still. Besides, I've never been to Yellow Creek before, and there's so many cattle-paths—they all look the same. But you've been there on Ted, and I know *he'll* take me."

Bright and early next morning saw the Woman in the saddle. The wagon-trail past the buttes and across Thunder Creek she couldn't miss if she tried, and when Ted turned off on a narrow cattle-path he seemed to know where he was going, so she rode with a loose rein. Sure enough, she soon heard a dog bark and the neighbour woman's voice saying: "Lay down there!" She was working in the garden but put away her hoe and showed where to tie Ted in the barn and helped to feed him hay.

The two women went to the house together, for it was time

to get dinner. "The men're away fencing some'eres," the neighbour woman confided as she opened the door.

Small was no trouble to the men. She played with Kitty, dressed her dolls, and read a bit of a fairy-tale book, while her father and his helper drove the heavy posts and strung the wire.

The job was finished early, and the Man began to cook supper with the help of Small, who handed him salt and pepper for the meat and set the table.

It was almost September, and the days were drawing in. The Woman was to be back by dark, and they waited till nearly eight o'clock before eating, by which time Small was getting sleepy.

"Is Mummy coming home very soon?" she asked, as she slipped down from the table.

"Just about the time you get into bed, chick," said the Man.

The evening chores were done. Small was in bed, hugging Kitty. The Man had not the heart to take the little grey beast to the barn that night, and after peeking in and hearing the steady purr from the bed he closed the door softly.

Ten o'clock came. The Man could stand it no longer. He started up, put on his hat and his chaps, and stepped out. A light still blinked from the bunkhouse. The Lad was reading in bed.

Before he had taken six steps towards the barn the Man heard a whinny from the corral, and then an answer from the dark hillside. Must be range horses, he thought. She'd never come home over the ridge, with a good wagon-trail around the bottom! Nevertheless he shouted, and a high, musical little "Ooo-hoo" came back. A minute later he saw her white Stetson in the gloom. Mentally kicking himself for being a nervous fool, he opened the east gate.

"Sorry I'm late." The Woman's voice was calm and easy. "I stayed late. We had such fun—she's a nice person. She told me all about being saved and talking with tongues! Then there was a mad fox—at least, she said it was a 'rabies fox.' It was in the barnyard and wouldn't go away. So she went after it with a club, and it went into a shed and she slammed the door. The men shot it afterwards, poor thing."

"Yes. . . . But how in hell did you come riding down the hill? There's no trail that way. You might have got lost or hurt or—something," he concluded lamely. They were unsaddling Ted. The saddle-fork was full of spruce needles, twigs, and leaves. So was Ted's mane—and her riding boots.

"Oh well, you see," she answered calmly, "you can blame your famous Ted for that! It was dark when I left. I crossed Thunder Creek, but I don't think it was at the ford, and then started to climb the hill. But I knew we weren't on the trail, and I had to leave it to Ted. All I knew was it was steep, and so bushy I had to tie my hat down with a string. Up and up we went, me bumping my knees on the trees. Somehow we arrived at the top—but where on earth we were I hadn't the foggiest notion. I felt by Ted's stride that he was sure enough where he was going, so I just let him. I must say I seem to have been crashing through alders and willows and deadfall for hours—but when I came out on the open ridge and saw the light, well, you can imagine!"

"The old cuss!" exclaimed the Man. "One side of a triangle may look shorter to a horse than two, but it takes twice as long, and it's a wonder you have any skin on your nose—or hair on your head," he added.

He knew she had been a little frightened and spoke lightly; but in all his conjectures as to what might have befallen her he had to admit he had never thought of a rabid fox; and he knew that the merest graze from such an animal's tooth could be a serious matter.

He was not surprised when a few days later a warning came over the radio that an outbreak of rabies actually had started. Everyone was warned not to touch or try to skin any dead animal.

The neighbours at Yellow Creek lost a cow from the disease. They said the poor beast, which they isolated in a corral, never stopped bawling and frothing and butting at the rails till it died.

And shortly after, when they were stacking oat bundles, the Man and the Lad killed a sick fox with their pitchforks. It was a beautiful silver, and it kept playing around the horses' feet. The Man was in fear of one of the team being bitten, but luckily they lured it into the open and pierced it through.

The Lad stooped to pick it up, but his boss shouted: "Don't touch it!" and picked it up with his fork, carrying it far into a clump of bush and roughly burying it.

The epidemic passed. Kitty, who had been kept confined, was allowed out again.

Chapter 24

The summer passed on golden wings, as it does for those who must meet each stage of growth and change head-on. With over two hundred cultivated acres in hay and grain, every moment counted, each fair day had to be used; and when rain interrupted haying or harvest there was always the new breaking to work down or more fence to be built to protect the expanding acreage.

In September the second-hand binder clattered its way through the tall, rank oats, dropping its neatly tied sheaves into rows which, once stooked, were safe from the weather until they could be stacked.

The Highland bulls had paid for themselves in more ways than one. The calf crop had more bone. And they were free of the tendency towards sickle-hocks and short legs which the Angus had inherited from bulls bred too fine, conforming too closely to the small, neat, blocky type beloved of show-breeders; this tendency had encouraged the bane of the range cattleman —dwarfism.

True to their hill-ancestry, the Scottish bulls and their cross-bred offspring led the way up to the high ranges for the summer, so that, except for the depredations of the wild horses, the grass of the sidehills and valleys grew thick and untouched through the growing-month of June. It now lay cured by the August sun to provide winter rustling and early spring grazing when the upland growth still stood matted, sere, and unpalatable.

The garden had been good, and there would be potatoes, carrots, and beets enough and to spare. Butter for winter filled the big crocks down cellar.

The only losses had been two calves killed by bears. And the foal. That still rankled.

Fall saw the men feverishly stacking the oat bundles. The weather was fine but was liable to break any day. It began to freeze at night, and the cow moose began to call to the fat bulls, which moved so stealthily and silently over the carpet of leaves that lay like golden guineas among the ghostly, pale boles of the poplars.

One late afternoon, as the men were topping a stack, they heard a cow moose call from Round Hill. The Man looked at the sky. "Still lacks an hour to sundown," he said, "but we'll quit early today. You put the teams in. We need meat. The weather will stay cool enough, I think."

His companion nodded as, just then, they heard the answering grunt of a bull from the top of the coulee.

The bull fell not fifty yards from the wagon-trail. They skinned and butchered it in the bush, hanging the meat high to chill. But the hide they rolled up and threw on the woodshed roof—next time old Atchikoos came by he would take it back to the Crying Girl Prairie and Mary would tan it for winter moccasins.

Winter could come now, early or late, for they had meat, vegetables, and butter for themselves, and hay and oats for the stock. Even if they were caught with a few stooks out, these could be hauled on sleighs.

On the night of November 10th it snowed. Not deep, but it was winter's visiting card. It would be anybody's guess whether it would stay or go, whether a brief Indian summer might follow. But in the meantime the big oil-drum heater would make a good place to sit by when evening chores were done.

The Man went out next morning into a white world. It did not surprise him. He had slept heavily and the house had felt warm and very still, while the usual barnyard noises had been muffled; he knew the signs. When the wind tore at the house roof, when the trees creaked, when the moon shone brightly, sending silvered fingers to move slowly across his bed, the floor, and the walls, then he slept lightly, alert to every sound, translating squeaks and groans and rustlings into the fraternal rubbing together of trees, a bull scratching on a corral, a horse stamping in the barn, or mice at play.

Now he stood in the snow, his back to the fast-growing light, his face to the west. All the tree limbs were laden, drooping under their soft covering. Each willow bush was bowed to the ground and looked like an igloo. The clouds, grey and desolate, were slowly lifting, breaking a little, letting fall a few tardy and desultory flakes which, touching his face, slowly melted.

The Man was looking for some cattle he had seen the evening before, some twenty head which had been crowding the fence. In anticipation of the impending snow, the older cows instinctively at this season drew nearer to home in hopes of feed. But it didn't do to start feeding too early, for then, even if the weather improved, cattle were loath to return to rustling for themselves, and the six inches of snow, which now lay over the range and the meadows, topping each remaining stook with white, was as yet no impediment to grazing. He had in mind driving this bunch across the valley to the big swamp where the flanking spruce gave protection from the wind and where the tall grass was still green and sweet at the bottom.

But all he saw now were two cows, with white blankets over their backs. They were neither lying snugly nor grazing, but rather wandering listlessly back and forth like people who have lost something and must search within a known boundary. He could not see their calves, which at this age should also have been up and about.

The Man went in to breakfast, wondering why these two had elected to remain by the fence, in almost the same place where poor Susie, the wall-eyed cayuse, had looked in vain for her foal that pleasant summer's day. He didn't like the look of it and was strangely silent over his porridge and eggs.

From near the buildings, almost to the creek, there was a

break in the hayfield formed by a low, rolling ridge of prairie which the Man had considered too rough to cultivate. Also, the prairie chickens danced each spring on its smooth, short-grassed knolls among the wild crocuses, and later the wild flax nodded in blue ecstasy with lacy bedstraw. He could not bring himself to tear up with cold steel such a little garden of beauty, such a flowery prairie, for the sake of a load or two of fodder.

As the Man, on Monte, rode along the south slope of this low, undulating elevation, the summer warmth still furtively hiding below the snow began to assert itself. Now a cool, damp mist began to shroud the creek and the farther tree clumps, spreading into the little hollows so that the two solitary cows beyond the fence seemed to come and go strangely, wraith-like.

Monte without warning stopped in his stride, pricking his ears towards the north-west, towards the obscured bend of Wild Horse Creek, lost somewhere behind the last of the knolls.

"What's up?" the Man said softly, and touched the horse with his spur. But Monte only flinched a little, wrinkled the hide of his flank, without moving.

The Man slipped from the saddle, led Monte back to a still lower spot, and dropped the reins for an anchor. He levered a shell into his rifle-breech as quietly as possible. The two cows, nearer now, stared at him through the fence. His every instinct told the Man that *something* was beyond that rise of ground north of the gate. He felt his scalp prickle as, bent low, he worked his way uphill. He wished his heart would not thump so loudly.

Then, lying prone, he peered over the hillock, and he could have laughed aloud at his precautions. There, on a lower knoll, about a hundred yards away and separated from him by a narrow draw, lay—a bunch of cattle! Some were dark, some the colour of tawny grass. A bunch of cross-bred yearlings for sure —they came all colours from black to brindle and dun. But they had no business in the meadow. The fence must be down —perhaps that short rail-fence from the corner to the creek. Damn!

The Man was about to rise when a wisp of fog blotted out the scene, and with it came the roaring, eery howl of timber wolves, so close that the cacophony made him flinch.

Wolves! And they must have killed that night or they would not be here, sleeping off a big feed. Now they were getting ready to move away.

For a full three minutes the weird primeval music shuddered up and down from the canyon to the little hills and back, and the Man heard an answer flung back from the west, from across the creek—evidently the Black Wolf lay there, a little apart as usual, on his lookout. The Man was steady now, his scalp relaxed. My God!—how nearly he'd blundered! He rose to one knee, rifle ready.

The fog began to rise but settled again. The Man glanced over his shoulder. Monte still stood like a rock where he'd been left.

And now a tiny breeze sprang up, and the silver wisps were driven high. Then he saw the wolves plainly, counted them below him as they sat on their haunches like dogs. There were six—three dark grey, one black, and two yellowish-grey. Picking one of the greys, the nearest, he fired. The wolf dropped. He fired again and missed, as the rest scattered like chaff, fanning out, dodging, twisting, making desperately for the brush along the creek bank. He reloaded, looking sharply across the creek to where the last howl had sounded. He was just in time to see the Black Wolf leap to his feet and run north along the top of the bank on the other side of the creek. He led with his sights and pulled the trigger for the third time. The wolf stumbled, then turned a complete somersault.

"Got him!" the Man breathed. He ran to where the wolves had been lying and stood looking down at what he had shot.

It was the three-footed bitch, all grizzled about the muzzle, her dry dugs showing her to have been many times a mother. "The old she-wolf herself," said the Man slowly. "Poor old girl! She was a game 'un."

He strode towards Monte, who was sweating as the waves of wolf-stench came to him. Quickly the Man slipped into the saddle and turned the horse towards the creek. Monte sidled and blew as he avoided the body of the bitch.

Rifle in hand the Man dismounted and crossed the gurgling stream. He expected to see the Black Wolf lying dead among the scrub, but was disappointed. Not a sign did he see till he came across the bounding tracks of the wolf as he left his bed, and then, following these, the mark made by the animal's somersault—a deep dent in the snow. He looked for blood and found none. The wolf must have leapt far and wide, for here all tracks ended.

Circling ever wider, the Man continued to search for the tracks of his enemy's landing, but found none, though he quartered as far as forty feet from where his shot had taken the animal in full flight. He stood irresolute, puzzled. Had this mysterious and clever animal played some last trump card, some desperate trick born of necessity? Had it launched itself into the creek, never touching the thirty feet of bank, and plunged into the narrow waters flowing at least twelve feet to the right?

That was the only conclusion the Man could reach. He knew a wolf could go a long way even though shot to death; he knew any animal might bleed inwardly and never leave a tell-tale drop of blood; but if alive, it *had to* leave tracks somewhere. He was positive he had hit the wolf, and hit it hard. He had heard the thud of the slug. And moreover, had he missed, the bullet would have left its mark as it ploughed through the snow, and search as he might he could not find such a mark.

He scrambled down to the creek's edge, but whatever secret the dark, swift water held, it ran steadily on and betrayed nothing. He hardly thought even an uninjured animal would try to breast the strong current, but nevertheless he followed upstream for a hundred yards in the direction the rest had fled, but to no avail. The banks showed not as much as a mink's tracks on the new snow.

If the wolf were alive, it must have scrambled out somewhere. If it were dead, it should have hung up on one of the many logs which lay with one end half-submerged in the water. The Man turned back and followed the creek downstream towards the canyon, alert to the slightest misplacement of snow at the water's edge, examining each log for signs of snow being brushed away. All was as blank as a sheet of white paper, except for the trackless water itself. Deep into the canyon he scrambled, now almost on hands and knees, until the narrow cleft became so obstructed with dead and tangled willows that further progress became almost impossible, and he finally turned his back on that dark and labyrinthine place.

Was it possible that a chest-shot had so shattered the animal's lungs that, following his great leap, he had sunk like a stone, to be carried along the depths which ran below the impeding logs and trash?

The Man only knew that, in death as so often in life, the old clan leader had left not a clue to his whereabouts. A wolf is no otter to remain indefinitely under water; no eagle to take wing and disappear into the blue.

Although he felt in his bones that the feud had ended in victory for himself, the Man felt little satisfaction and stood for a moment or two, drenched with sweat, feeling cheated and still puzzled. He could only hope that at least his old enemy had met a clean death, worthy of his long and cunning fight for the survival of his race.

The Man remembered the cows now. Shivering slightly he climbed the bank, threading his way between the brittle saskatoon stems and the clumps of bear-berry to avoid the avalanches of wet snow which cascaded at every touch. Suddenly, he was brought to himself by a loud bawl.

Dreading what he might see, the Man slipped through the fence. Cattle- and wolf-tracks were mingled in the trampled snow. A quick look at the cows satisfied him that they had not been torn, but even as he turned from them he saw the shambles of blood-stained snow to his right. One big calf lay apparently dead, the tendons of one hind leg severed and its throat laid open. Twenty yards farther lay another, of which little was left but the head, ribs, and pelvis, one leg lying apart.

Red anger in his heart, the Man let the cows through the gate and followed them as they stepped quickly across the meadow in the direction of the corral, new hope in their eyes, perhaps from some memory of last year's weaning, when their calves had been taken from them and corralled at the buildings.

Probably they had bawled last night. If they had, even his keen ears might not have heard, for the snow would have blotted out sound as well as sight.

He stamped into the porch, seized a hammer, and quickly drew the nails from the board which only he knew. Reaching under the floor he brought to light the can of strychnine he had up till now been so loath to use. With this in his pocket and a skinning knife in his belt he rode west once more.

The crippled calf was not dead. It raised its head briefly but silently and rolled an eye in terror.

"Poor devil," said the Man, and severed the gashed throat, completing the wolf's work.

This was good beef, not to be wasted. The calf was a good five hundred pounds' weight, almost ready to wean. Deftly he skinned out the hind quarters, severed them, and set them aside on a clean patch of snow.

With great care he made incisions with his knife between the ribs, in the liver, about the shoulders, sifting into each as much strychnine as the knife's point would pick up.

Too much, he knew, was no good. A wolf would vomit it up and live, twice as cunning, to kill again.

He put a few doses into what was left of the other carcass.

Then he rode over to the poor dead bitch, already stiffening, skinned her, and put a couple of doses between her ribs. He knew that wolves will often eat their own dead.

The whole operation was, he also knew, only a shot in the dark. Would the young wolves, left to themselves, return to the kill? Never, if the bitch had survived. Never, if their father was still alive. But he fondly hoped that the Black Wolf lay drowned somewhere in the creek.

Yes, this might be worth the trouble, he thought, as he rose to his feet, almost overpowered by the carrion smell of the old she-wolf. In spite of Monte's objections he threw the reeking hide over the saddle and mounted, jerking up the horse's head as it attempted to buck.

Before he went back for the third time he washed the wolf-taint from his hands and tied two gunny-sacks to the saddle.

"Here's meat," he said to the Woman, dumping the heavy bags on the kitchen floor.

"What's been going on?" she asked. "Shooting—and riding back and forth?"

He told her.

That night as he turned over in bed he heard the wolves howl.

The Man was away at dawn, rifle ready. He had taken a chance and left the gate open the night before so that he would not have to dismount. As he rode through it something seemed to be half jumping, half struggling along, just west of the hill. He shot—too hurriedly—and missed. The young black wolf, for it was he, recovered and ran straight west for the timber on Willow Creek.

The country was broken here, low hills and shallow runways with clumps of willows. He sighted the wolf twice more, sometimes staggering and weaving from side to side, but still making good progress; and both times he pulled the trigger—but to no avail. As the beast disappeared into the heavy scrub it seemed to be travelling better than ever.

The Man rode on.

Well, all his luck hadn't left him! Three young wolves lay as dead as mutton. A grizzly-grey one and two tawny yellow with dark manes. Riding a little circle he noticed that, scattered as they were, they lay with their noses pointed in the same direction, as if they had all been intent on some favoured spot when death overtook them as they crawled and staggered from their feast. That direction was the canyon rim; he would remember that.

Then he came across several piles of half-chewed meat mixed with white froth. This was what the black youngster had evidently vomited, saving his life. Likely he had taken a double dose. Three pitiful magpies and a south-bound rough-leg hawk also lay near the bait, stiff and with clenched claws.

That was poison. A ghastly thing!

There was still one wolf to account for, a grey, and this he found dead by the lean, ribby carcass of the three-footed bitch. What had given him life had likewise meted out agonizing death.

Now the Man rode to the canyon rim. Right in line with those mutely pointed snouts he saw a great spruce reared above the depth, and walking straight towards it he peered

over the rim into the gloom and saw that the base of the trunk was far below, only a few feet above the pale gleam of the murky water. On an impulse he climbed down among the rocks and the dark, mossy deadfall of years. Something gleamed whitely, and he saw a rib-bone, and just beyond that, the cracked skull of a foal. Crouching at the base of the spruce, he saw what he half expected now, the mouth of the den.

The loss of the brood-mare's foal, the wolf sleeping on the haystack, the tracks of early spring by the ford, all were now explained.

Who would think that wolves could den so close to a building and not show themselves more? This had been artful survival, but it was over now—with only one wolf alive from the finest litter the old girl had raised.

But never again, he hoped, would his arch-enemy, the Black

Wolf, play his tricks. Never again would he force a foal over a cutbank or canyon—as he evidently had forced Susie's foal, leaving neither track nor trace.

His hopes were justified.

But it was not till the next spring that the Lad, tending his beaver traps, found the remains of the old cattle-killer washed up on the gravel bar at the junction with Middle Fork, nearly half a mile downstream.

The bounty came to $125. Blood-money, the Man thought, and gave the cheque to the Woman.

The skinned wolf carcasses were thrown, for the time being, on the bunkhouse roof.

Chapter 25

The team plunged through the drifts at the foot of Moose Point. The harness bells pealed happily, and the sleigh tipped to one side. The man side-stepped and threw his weight on the other, and the runners righted themselves. The passengers laughed; but at that moment—above the merriment, the creaking, and the snorts of the horses—the Man, ears attuned and senses alert, heard the sound he had been dreading . . .

A shot, muffled by distance, but unmistakably a rifle shot.

He had said to the Lad last night: "Not till we are well on our way. I don't want the women to hear it. They'd ask questions." The Lad had nodded, sympathy in his eyes.

So now it was done.

Old Fox had been more than a horse. Now he lay in some unknown place—trust the Lad for that—some place where no-one, least of all himself, would be apt to stumble upon a reminder.

The Man knew this was the merciful thing, yet he felt guilty at the thought of that long, sober, blazed face and the honest eyes now closed for ever.

"If only horses could live as long as men!" he thought, and with that began to run over in his mind the many mounts he had outlived. Little Roany, way back in those Cypress Hills days. Pasquia Hills Jack, the big bay, a patrol horse without peer. Mohawk and Blue Charlie, Hornet and Kip, and Vinegar the tall Bar Cee from the foothills. These and many more passed before the eyes of his memory this morning—buckskins and blacks, bays and chestnuts. Some rough, some flighty, others mild yet fiery, but all faithful if you knew them, and understood their kinks of temperament. As they galloped by his mind's eye, he wondered how soon that loosened troop would be joined by Ted and Robin and Monte and the colt he was now breaking, Traveller . . .

It was the week before Christmas, and the family were on their way to the town, as the little cross-roads settlement was now called. The larder had to be replenished and surreptitious treats bought for the festive season.

Snuggled down in the hay-filled box, the Woman and Small chattered away under the heavy steer-robes between peeks at the sliding landscape. The Man drove standing, feet well apart, the better to see the winding, snow-shrouded trail and to determine the lay of the drifts or any impediments ahead.

There were plenty of these. Every time the wind blew, more trees fell, and showed only as bumps under the snow. Spotting them the Man would call "Hang on!" and up would go the front of the sleigh, then the back, making the passengers roll and laugh. But the greener trees—spruce or poplar—often broke halfway up, perhaps weakened by a woodpecker's nesting hole, and these would fall with their crests across the trail, held at the large end by their trunks perhaps six, perhaps twelve feet above the ground, effectively blocking the trail at breast height. Then the team had to stop, while the Man reached for his axe and his cross-cut saw. For ten minutes the silence of the forest would ring to the sound of axe blows and the sharp whine of the saw, till, sawing and chopping alternately, the Man had severed both ends of the log and rolled the centrepiece off the trail's edge. A word to the horses, and the bells would jingle again.

So, with many such stops and starts and a break for a noontime boil-up of tea and a forkful of hay for the team, they arrived at the Cutbank stopping house for the night.

The lady of the house said: "Land's sakes, we was expecting you folks! I says to Jasper only this morning, them folks is bound to be down along most any time with Christmas so close! You just come on in and take off your things. I'll cook a mess o' chicken and fix a salad—I got plenty garden sass and cabbage down cellar." To the Man: "Put your team in. Jasper's out to the barn, he'll help you."

Jasper didn't. He was an aging, portly man with the air and face of a butler. "Nice to see you," he said listlessly, and put out a flabby hand. "Put your team in the back stall. And say, I was a-goin' to clean the barn, but my heart kinda acts up, and then my arthuritis, the son-of-a-gun, keeps a-naggin' of me . . ."

The Man grinned, took the five-tined fork from the other's limp hand, and quickly cleaned the three stalls, loading the soiled bedding on the sleigh by the door. He was hungry, and he was tired. But he knew his host. If you didn't lend the old humbug a hand there'd be veiled hints all through supper about the pain and trouble of having other folks' horses to look after, the way they mucked up the barn!

The fact that Jasper's visitors were really cutomers, who paid well for both barn and table accommodation, didn't enter into that worthy's calculations.

During supper the lady of the house began to give out the local news. She dwelt at some length and with evident satisfaction on the matter of a neighbour's girl who had been too "forward" with the U.S. troops and had finally taken the "wrong turn." This topic exhausted, she launched into bits and pieces of gossip, jumping rapidly from this subject to that. "You folks know how much old Charlie got fur them two fed steers?" she commenced. "No? Well he's a close-mouthed old cuss. He don't ever go to town—Mitchell drops his mail here. Oh yes, them steers; well he got *twenty-six cents* a pound—I seen the cheque," she added slyly. She rose to fill the potato bowl, while the Man wondered if she had steamed open old Charlie's envelope from the Edmonton Stockyards. The hostess seated herself again, pushed back her hair from her flushed forehead, said, "Pa, pass them buns to the little girl," and resumed her gossip. "Them folks across the river done real well trapping—got a fourteen-fifteen fox a'ready. They sends 'em in to town with Big Les, from the mine—and say! I near forgot! Les was a-telling me some feller told him in the beer parlour as how them hoss traders done got in some kinda scrap. Didn't know what. Some said as how one was dead. Seems they got a quarrelling they two, and there'd been a fight—but land's sake, you couldn't hardly believe it was that bad. Them boys was allus on the prod, fightin' an feudin', fur as I know. Me and Jasper, we used to know some of their folk down in Montany and Wyoming, and they was allus a wild lot, the hull boodle."

And so on for half an hour, until exhausted and breathing hard from her exertions, the stout lady finally jumped to her feet and exclaimed: "Land's sakes, them dishes!" with a sharp glance at the Woman. Meals were seventy-five cents at the stopping house, but "company" helped with dishes, which was "visiting," not working.

Next day in town the Man went for the mail, while the Woman and Small shopped. There was plenty of talk on the street about an oil-strike up north on the Yukon road. Striding through the little throng at the post office, nodding here, hulloing there, he opened his box. The usual advertizing folders. Blue air-mail letters from overseas. A catalogue, a handful of Christmas cards, the papers. "The Cattleman" from Calgary, and an envelope he knew contained a cheque from the editor of that ranchers' journal for which he often wrote articles. A notice of a meeting of the Cattlemen's Association. And finally, a long, brown envelope with OHMS at the top.

At the hotel he opened first an air mail postmarked "Fitzroy Crossing, West Australia." It was from the Boy, who, after his service in Korea, had sought new fields for ranching operations in a country where cattlemen were still honoured as the mainstay of industry, and likely to remain so for a while.

Reading, he was transported, and saw the spinifex, the emeus, and the kangaroos, and the "Abo" stock-riders who dashed across the flimsy blue sheet. The Boy could write descriptively.

The Woman and Small entered, tired and flushed from their tour of the Co-op and the Hudson's Bay store. Strange parcels were hurriedly hidden in the baggage while the Man pretended calm unconcern.

Now he tore across the OHMS, drew out a typewritten sheet, and quickly read the few lines above the corporal's dashing signature, which ended with "NCO i/c Detachment RCMP."

"The corporal wants to see me," he said.

"What on earth for?" the Woman queried.

"Dunno, but I'll pop into the barracks."

He took down his old fur cap, shrugged into his canvas coat, and left.

"Glad to see you so soon," was the corporal's greeting. "Only posted that letter yesterday, on the chance you'd be in."

"Yes—what can I do for you?" asked the Man.

"Well," answered the policeman, "first, did you hear about those pals of yours—the horse traders?"

"Only a rumour at the stopping house. Said there'd been a fight. . . . Why?"

"Those fellows are both dead, that's why," replied the corporal grimly. "We don't quite know what happened. They were a bit 'bushed,' y'know. Hardly ever went anyplace. Didn't make friends. Anyway, old Martinson—who has a trap line up that way—called with some mail for them. No smoke. No sign of life. So he went in the shack. It was cold, and on the bed was one of the fellows, half-frozen and raving. Martinson couldn't make out what he said. He looked him over and found he'd a leg all swollen up and black with gangrene. Couldn't find the other fellow and figured he'd gone to the settlement for help. So he loaded the guy on his dog-toboggan and mushed to the Yukon road—the cabin's only 'bout ten miles south, in the bush. He stopped a truck and the fellow was brought in, but he died in hospital that night, still raving. No-one had seen the other guy.

"So I took one of my chaps and went up in there myself. We didn't want too much talk right then. You know the papers . . .

"Didn't take long to find the other man. Frozen stiff, he was, under a tarp in the shed, with a bullet hole in his head. This fellow must have shot at his brother from outside. The other fellow was apparently standing in the doorway, for the bullet went through the fleshy part of his leg and we found it in the back wall. Then the wounded guy had his turn, and he sure took good aim! How he dragged the body in the shed isn't hard to reckon. A flesh wound don't stiffen for some time, and these kind are as tough as lobo wolves, anyway.

"He must have figured he could doctor a flesh wound himself, but he didn't know what old Doc found at the inquest—that the bullet took out a chip of bone. So instead of getting better it got worse, till finally he couldn't even get up to keep the

stove going, and it near thirty below. He'd have frozen to death anyway, shape he was in.

"Yes, we found the rifles. Winchesters, 1895 models. They're over there." The corporal jerked his head towards the corner of the office. "Both had one empty shell in the breech.

"Looking over their old letters we managed to get the address of an older sister, married, at Great Falls—you knew they came from Montana? We've notified her. She doesn't think she can get up. Says she's ill. So she asks us to sell whatever property they have and send her the money. Says she's the only next-of-kin.

"I checked with the Land Office and find they were only squatters, so there's no land. And the buildings are only sheds—log, with dirt roofs—and a mess of corrals. So that leaves only stock. Just horses, I guess. They had only one old mowing machine for putting up a little horse-feed along the creek. It isn't worth dragging out.

"That's the picture." And the corporal leaned back, putting a match to his pipe.

"Yes . . . poor devils. . . . But where do *I* come in?" asked the Man, turning over the story in his mind.

The corporal grinned. "*You* come in as government representative—or hired man—for gathering the stock," he replied. "I am authorized to pay you"—he glanced at a typed sheet—"to pay you four dollars per head for every horse you bring out—bar any of your *own* you find, eh?"

"Have a heart, Corporal!" interjected the rancher. "I've got my hands full with cattle this winter, and anyway it's a hell of a time to round up horses. Why, even a grained saddle-horse couldn't make many miles in this deep snow."

"Who said to round up this winter?" The corporal's grin was broader now. How these old stockmen loved to jump the gun! "No," he said. "Early spring will do. Those cayuses have run loose every winter, so they can this. The worst that can happen is Martinson may shoot an old mare for bait. Let him. He's earned it. Nobody knows how many horses these fellows had. And from what you yourself hinted to me there may be lots which don't carry their W-J brand."

The Man was thinking of his two fillies. They'd be mares now, probably with colts. "I'll do it," he said. "But I'll need some help. I'd like to get those boys from Thunder Creek. They're good."

"I reckoned you would." The corporal's grin was gone now, replaced by a relaxed smile. "Get who you like. I'll pay 'em five bucks a day and two bucks each for grub. Keep track of it and send in the bill when you're through. We'll want the nags gathered and trailed down here to the stampede corrals. Bring everything on that range, see? And we'll cut out their stuff and have a sale. Anything not carrying the W-J we'll advertize and the owners can get them on proof of claim and four bucks apiece. Whatever isn't sold or claimed we'll ship to the cannery at Grande Prairie, and the proceeds will go to—what's the term?—oh yes, the Consolidated Fund of the Province. That's the set-up. O.K.?"

"O.K.," agreed the Man. "I'll send you word in late March or April. It will depend on the depth of snow and the creeks. Too early, we'll play out horses. Too late, we may drown some."

Chapter 26

The young wolf, black like his father and almost as big, was ill. He had been ill for many weeks. He was sore all over, the sour taste and the bitter memory of that burning dose still in his throat. Never again would he touch a piece of free meat or return to a kill. Only what he killed himself, what he fed on at once, was safe.

Too weak to hunt bigger game now, he lived on smaller fry—snowshoe rabbits, grouse if he could catch one, but mostly on the beaver-brown voles. These were now at the high point of their cycle. The little rodents had a maze of runways under the snow, from which they gnawed at the roots or chewed the shattered seeds of wild grasses beneath the flattened and faded herbage. It was not cold under there, and their thick, furry coats could not be ruffled by the harsh winds which whipped at the face of the well-packed drifts.

On warmer days the small animals popped out of the little holes which led them to the surface of the snow, where they played or blinked at the sun, or simply squatted to let its rays warm their small, palpitating bodies. The low December sun greeted them but briefly, and with the fall of dusk and the hooting of the owls, the voles disappeared once more into their tunnels.

The wolf smelt them out, dug through the snow, and seized

the chattering rodents, tossing them down his throat. Alive or dead, they were all the same to him, so long as they quieted the winter-hunger which gnawed at him. Paralyzed with fear, it was all the same to the voles as well—for the imminence of death brings anaesthesia to the wild things.

A northern shrike, all dressed in greys and whites, hook-billed as any hawk, often followed the wolf, fluttering above his head, ready to pounce on any vole the wolf might overlook while occupied in jumping, big pads together, on the scurrying clans.

The wolf stiffened at a sound which came to him through the dimness of twilight. Turning, he looked east across the creek and saw the team trotting north from Deep Springs. It was the clinking of their heel-chains which had made him pause in his mousing. The team stopped at some piles of cut brush and dry sticks which had been cleared off the new breaking. He saw the Man throw one—three—five dark objects upon the largest pile. There was a sparkle of light, like a falling star, and then a puff of smoke.

The team turned for home in the gloom, not yet so dark, but they showed as a moving blur against the snow, the heel-chains again noisy on the frosty air.

Before the moon rose the wind changed, and the wolf could smell the smoke from the now leaping fire, which lit the surrounding snow to blood-red. He watched, fascinated, still as a dark rock. Smoke was harmless. Thick and black it billowed, shot with fleecy white where dry willow-sticks blazed.

The wolf was about to return to his mouse-hunt when he detected another odour, rank above the familiar one of burning willow and poplar. A homely smell, a cadaver-like wolfy smell. A smell which made him aware of his loss, of his three-footed dam, of his tawny brothers, of the old, safe den. But he noticed that the wolf-smell was not quite that; for it was more acrid, more bitter, lacking the familiar sense of warmth and safety. Something told him that all was not right here.

He loped into the valley. The scent was stronger. Although fascinated and half-eager to greet whatever he should meet, his craftiness and suspicion still gave him pause, and he halted for a moment fifty feet from the smouldering brush pile.

Step by cautious step he advanced once more with outthrust, quivering muzzle, circling the fire, always a little closer.

The flames subsided to a few feeble flickers, reflected in the wolf's searching eyes.

The ashes glowed, dull-red.

Half-buried within them lay burnt, dark things. Were they slow-smouldering logs, half-rotten, damp?

Something rolled out beyond the fire, smoking. The wolf-stench was stronger, the smoke reeking of it as the brief wind sank to rest.

The wolf circled again, three times. It was bitter cold. A half-moon shed its cold light from above, and the animal's shadow, dark on the snow, enhanced the eeriness of the scene, as if two wolves walked cheek by jowl.

The thing no longer smoked. The wolf drew closer, hackles raised. On his belly he crept, touched the grisly thing with his nose, and leapt back, growling.

He crept up again. The thing was still hot, but he turned it over and over with quick dabs of his paw. The heat frightened him, and puzzled, he withdrew a few steps. Then he raised his snout, and with half-shut eyes, sent forth a long and quavering howl, wrenched from the depth of his being. Again and yet again he howled, but the only answer was the cold rustling of the aurora overhead.

The Man heard the howl, and half raised himself from his warm bed. "That damn wolf," he muttered, and slept again.

The following night was dark and cloudy, but the wolf padded once more to the valley floor, drawn by an irresistible longing for companionship.

The ashes were cold now. He tested them with a front foot, then took two more steps. The grey fluff stung his nostrils. He nosed the dark things one by one and knew them for what was left of his litter-mates; charred and horrible.

He turned away, paced around the charnel heap, and howled as he had done before.

All night he padded back and forth from his mousing in the willows nearby to the dark circle of melted snow, its edges glazed to sharp ice which tinkled under his feet. Before dawn he left.

At dusk that day a coyote trotted over to investigate and dragged one black body out onto the snow. But the wolf, returning once more, gave chase, and the prairie jackal tucked in his tail and fled.

At breakfast next day the Man said: "That damn lone wolf. I reckoned he would have left before. He's been hanging around for weeks. I took those carcasses up to burn two or three days ago, and now he's just hanging around up there. Did you hear him last night and the night before?"

The Lad nodded. "I heard him. Can't I set a trap?"

The Woman said: "Poor thing! He sounds so heartbroken, and he has no old wolf to follow, or maybe he'd move off."

The Man answered the Lad. "No. I doubt if a trap would take him. He'll be a smart wolf from now on, and if he brings a mate we'll have another lot as bad as the last. I'll see what a couple of snares can do."

He had two lynx snares he'd brought up years before but had never used. Range stock could be injured by those things. If a horse pawed into them they could tighten around its pastern, and they were made with a lock so they would not loosen up, but get tighter and tighter. A horse caught like that lost a hoof and had to be destroyed.

Hardening his heart, he took the snares up the valley and saw that the wolf used one trail to the ash pile and another to leave by.

Cunningly he set the wires, opened up their loops, tied the loose ends to chunks of broken logs which would give enough to prevent a hard jerk and a possible break. Then he camouflaged the loops with small twigs stuck in the snow or hung from the willows. With the turkey wing he had brought with him he smoothed over his tracks in the snow, backing up as he did so, until he reached his horse. He mounted and for a moment held in the restless horse while he surveyed his handiwork. Then, satisfied, he set off home for dinner.

It thawed a little that day, but by evening the mercury dropped again to minus zero.

The wolf approached with caution that night. All his senses told him to be careful, and at a point just short of the ashes, where his trail zig-zagged through heavy willows, he stopped dead. He could see nothing strange, but some instinct made him back up and work his way around. His premonitions had not played him false. There was a faint odour of man and long tracks—like a bear's—around the cold fire place.

Something else lying there, something dark, one corner moving slightly in the breeze, drew him onward. He did not know it was the man's red handkerchief, which had slipped unnoticed from a hip pocket. But the wolf did know the man-smell, and leaped backwards as if stung. Without another look he wheeled and ran, taking the trail he always did when leaving.

As he entered the red willows he was jerked backwards, his throat afire with pain. He lunged and lunged again. Something was suffocating him—something he could not see. Tongue out, gasping, he lunged a third time, propelling himself upward and forward with all the strength of his haunches.

There was a snapping sound, and he was free!

He did not check his headlong flight till he reached the high ridge beyond Big Prairie, beyond the West Fork, the ridge which thrust itself eastward from the mountains. The first real foothill . . .

The Man was half-sorry, half-glad to find the broken snare.

He looked at the lock. "Must have been cracked before," he muttered. "Not even a cougar could break a good steel lock." He should have checked better. And the log toggle frozen to the ground after the brief thaw had not given, but had held solid against the jerks.

The Woman said: "Thank goodness!" when she heard the story, and then put her hand over her mouth quickly.

Small piped up: "He didn't mean to be bad, Daddy–isn't it just nature for him to eat calves?"

The Lad said: "Maybe a trap?"

The lone wolf moused two more days on the ridge, hunting silently, sleeping much. He was not yet strong.

Within a week a chinook blew through a gash in the mountains. He was ready, rested and able to travel. He woke, stretched, and yawned, showing his strong young teeth below his drawn-back lip. He stood looking east to where three miles away Deep Springs Ranch lay shrouded in the grey of dawn.

It was seven o'clock, but the January sun would not show itself till after nine, although the Man was already astir. The wolf could see a tiny pin-point of light flickering between the house and the barn.

He howled once, long and quavering. It was his good-bye to Wild Horse Creek and the Cutbank.

The point of light stood still.

The wolf turned to a spruce stump, left his sign for the last time, and started for the west without looking back. By the time the sun was up he had made fourteen miles, had crossed the Elk-Run. He climbed the far bank, up and up to the desolate scrubby heights beyond. The mountains looked closer now, the sun touching their cold peaks with rose, their bases lost in the frost-fog.

The traveller crawled into a snow-free crevice among the rim-rocks and slept. He rose at mid-afternoon, hungry again. He killed and ate a snowshoe hare, gobbling fast, and then broke once more into the mile-eating wolf lope.

Just before dawn he stopped, looked to the sky, and howled several times in succession. Some of the lonesomeness had gone from his voice, which now had a more challenging, a more enquiring note. After each outburst he paused to listen, ears cocked and nose to the west.

At last, as he listened intently, he heard, far away and faint, an answering call.

He loped on.

Then on a high, windswept scree he found wolf-tracks; how many days old only the wind which had half obscured them knew. He followed them till he came to a dent in the snow. He lowered his muzzle, and such a wave of joy and desire flowed over him that all the loneliness of the past weeks was forgotten.

He must rest. He must hunt again. But tomorrow his journey would end where the mountain sheep kept their courts.

And old Atchikoos would soon be telling his tribesmen of a black wolf and his grey mate who never returned to a kill, no matter how tempting.

Chapter 27

The round-up riders were camped at the horse traders' untidy huddle of buildings.

It could take two weeks or more to gather the scattered bands of horses on this wild and rugged range. The corporal had sent two loads of baled hay by truck up the Yukon road, and a man with a team to haul them along the narrow bush-trail. There was also bagged oats for the riders' mounts.

It was gruelling work. Before daylight the men had to feed their mounts and throw some bales into the corral for the captives, followed by scoops of snow to slake their thirst. Range horses eat snow all winter.

Then they had to hurry through their coffee and hot-cakes, not sparing the cold-repelling syrup, after which they had to mount and ride for ten, twelve, fourteen hours, with a tight belt for noon. They could not stop to eat while running stock on the open range.

They ran one bunch for the best of two days before they coralled them. The leader, an old buckskin mare, a real old "ridge-runner," dodged up one coulee and down the next, in her endeavour to reach the high country. The riders had to twist and swing in their saddles to dodge the overhanging limbs. Their mounts grunted as they jumped the willow-tangles and big deadfall logs.

The wild bunch ran all out, and the riders had to follow, scarcely heeding the wicked, broken snags thrusting up through the snow, ready to disembowel any horse so unlucky as to slip or stumble. But when darkness fell that first day the horses were back where they had started from, for the old buckskin outsmarted the riders by swinging down a log-choked gully they had not known was there, and so back with her followers to the fastness of the heavy timber.

The bunch was located again early the next day, and soon the grain-fed saddle-horses began to gain; for like their riders', their blood was up. And when the old mare tried the ruse a second time one of the Thunder Creek boys was ready to turn her at the bottom. A two-year-old which had not entered the gully saw the mare turn, and tried to join her by leaping one of the deep, wide fissures at the gully's bottom. He was winded, his breathing a hoarse roar. He missed the far bank, clawed a moment with his front hooves, and fell backwards with a scream among a tangle of crossed logs. The Thunder Creek boy, hard on its heels, made the leap but did not pause. He knew the two-year-old's back was broken and it was already dead.

Now, with all the horses across the gully, the riders closed in. The country was more open, with willow and poplar only in clumps. The lead-mare hesitated. She had been dry last year and had no following-colt, as a young horse is called in its second year. She still had plenty of "gimp" in her, zest for the game. But the brood-mares were lagging, sweat dripping from them.

"Now!" yelled the Man, and with swinging ropes the men closed in tighter—two on the uphill side, one in the rear—swinging their ropes and letting out a shout that rang up the valley.

Under the hazing the lead-mare swung her head, tossed her tangled mane, and took off for the corrals.

The left side was safe, for already the creek was frothing and roaring under the spring sun and balmy winds from across the mountains. On they raced for a mile, the horses slipping and sliding in the thawing snow. A colt went down, and its mother paused, whinnying high and shrill. A pinto stallion nipped hard at the colt, which was on its feet in a second, crowding up to the mare.

The mad gallop subsided to a trot, and the trot to an uneasy walk, as the blown horses saw the corral gate loom before them in the twilight.

The last band to be brought in gave even more trouble. The creek was now booming, every coulee was in spate, the rushing waters bringing down trash, twigs, and dead grass, matted with leaves and foam. There was a sense of urgency in the men. This band came from the west, and the creek had to be crossed before they could reach the corrals. Another day, two days, and it might be impassable, for the smaller creeks are more dangerous and have cost more lives than real rivers, as every cowman knows.

The creek circled around the back of the corrals, and on its brink the leaders of the bunch braced their feet and turned away from the flood. Up and down they ran, trying to break back, but always balked by a weaving, swearing rider.

Finally, at the worst place, the lead-mare whinnied and was answered from the corral. She leapt wide and high, only to land in a deep pool below a bank which on the far side was too steep for a footing. In minutes the pool was full of horses. They could not swim upstream.

"Work 'em down, or they'll drown!" called the Man, and whirled his sodden rope.

The horses allowed the current to swing them downstream against their will. One or another kept trying to get back to the bank they had left.

"Keep 'em going!" called the Man again, yelling above the roar of the brown waters, and any noses touching the near bank felt the whip of a rope.

The horses drifted, squealing, around a bend. As the far bank lowered, the stallion found a footing and heaved himself, puffing, out of the flood. He ran a few steps and stood shivering, water pouring from mane and tail. One by one the others followed, pushing and scrambling. The whole band now paused, the mares searching out their colts with big eyes and tender mutterings. They were all right. Not so much as a colt snagged among the dry, waterlogged willows.

Again the men shouted. Muddy, tired, the horse-band trotted to join their neighbours behind bars.

As each band of horses was finally driven in, the Man noted each animal's colour, sex, weight, brand, and approximate age in his tally book.

There were few geldings, and these were either old and crippled or still too young for sale to the pack-outfits.

The Man sat on the top rail, satisfied. Not a man had been hurt, and below him were over 130 head of horses. They milled, squealing, kicking, as they got acquainted, for they had known other bands only as rivals for the sweetest grass and purest water.

The range had been cleaned, from the red stallion's band to the latest farm escapees.

Quite a few mares bore down-country brands, followed by yearlings and two-year-olds branded W-J. Those farmers' mares had worked hard for the traders!

But best of all, the Man found two lovely mares with his own LADDER S on their hips, followed by unbranded colts. The traders apparently didn't brand a colt till the mare had another. Foals were apt to suck all winter, and even the Law—which can't think—said that a sucker was the property of the man whose brand was on the mare. Brands can't be erased, and another brand cannot be put on an animal unless the brander can show proof of purchase. That was the Law—in theory, anyway. But this way was safe.

Looking over the bunch the Man made out two W-J yearlings, which now worked their way to his mares. There wasn't any doubt in his mind that these were his property, the mares' first foals. But he wouldn't try to claim them. Too hard to prove. Let the Montana woman have them, or their price. He was more than satisfied to have the mares and the young colts. He'd brand the little fellows as soon as this business was over and he got them home.

Chapter 28

The oil rumours began to grow as the giant young post-war boom got into the stride of maturity. There were now three wells only forty miles north of Deep Springs. Another was being drilled east of the Doig.

Oil survey crews were working everywhere, and one day a low-flying plane zoomed over the quiet ranch. Its shadow was dark on the hayfield; a shadow which made the Man think of that Bible story in which a cloud no bigger than a man's hand was to turn a desert to mud. This aircraft had a box-like contraption hanging some feet below it. The Man thought it was probably a camera, but the Lad, more interested in such things, said it was a seismograph instrument and the plane was on oil survey.

"Oh goodness," said the Woman, "I do hope they won't find anything here! I couldn't bear to have a smelly oil-well on our place—and all that noise! Why can't things stay as they are?"

The Man could not give—or take—much comfort from his remark that man is essentially discontented and unhappy, and this is what makes him so restless. He felt that worse was to come. He knew that with the disappearance of the wolves a link in the ecological chain binding the life of the valley together had been removed, and that the loose ends would never join again.

New methods were the fashion. Farm journals, pamphlets from the Department of Agriculture, lectures on the radio, were all stressing changes, new methods, more "up-to-date" operations. Use A1. Use DDT. Break the range-land up and sow to approved grasses. All these were new ways of doing old things, and probably no better. And with new ways came new diseases, new problems, leap-frogging over each other at a greater pace every day; all good for the industrial world, a world which thrived and grew fat on solving problems and creating new ones in the process. And the old, simple trinity of Man, God, and Earth was being shattered, probably beyond repair.

Since the wolves had left, the deer were increasing to the point where forty of them in one band would graze on the alfalfa, where formerly half a dozen had been the usual thing. This would mean more and more hunters screaming for access; and this, too, would be good business for industry, if not for the rancher.

And what if the last of the foxes, the last of the coyotes, were killed or forced out? That would leave only the hawks, the owls, and the ravens to deal with the rodents—the gnawing, tunnelling voles, the leaping bush hares.

Perhaps he, the rancher, would soon be in the way—would soon be under pressure to leave. Perhaps an oil town . . .

Trailing the steers to market this fall, the Man had the help of the boys from Thunder Creek. They were driving fifty head, mostly steers, with some yearling heifers and a few dry cows; for the Man was culling his herd carefully.

The Man was on "point," scouting ahead, the lead-steer following his every move. The Thunder Creek boys were on the flanks, while in the drag the Woman rode Monte, the snappy little black she hadn't wanted to ride two years ago. By her side Small sat steady Robin, now old and grey-muzzled. The Lad followed with the tent-wagon, his own saddle-horse tied behind.

The cattle were strung out, walking well and approaching Burnt Creek. Rounding the foot of the hills a sudden roar frightened them, and they hesitated, bunched up, looking this way and that. The Man heard a strange, deep noise. Surely not a wolf in broad daylight? He checked his horse and listened. No. It sounded like an engine.

"Cat!" yelled the Lad and the Thunder Creek boys in unison.

It was a bulldozer.

High above them, coming around a steep shoulder, a great juggernaut suddenly loomed dark against the sky; black, stinking diesel smoke trailed upward from a pipe. It came straight on without a pause. Making its own road it chugged on its way, the soft dirt of the hillside falling, tumbling in broken clods; small rocks, big rocks, stumps, and shale slid down, down, burying the yellow grass and levelling the old buffalo-trails, smirching the hillside, smothering the soft sages and the crocus plants which had bloomed all mauve each spring.

In one glance the Man took in the scene and spurred his horse. The frightened steers were breaking in every direction, tails up, eyes rolling at the sight and sound of the awful invader.

It took two hours of hard riding to round them up, and even so they lost one yearling in the brush.

"Let 'im go!" yelled the Man, coughing in the dust. "He'll either follow and catch up or find his way home! We'll push on before they spook again!"

There were only five miles to Thunder Creek. The Lad, who had tied his team in the willows and ridden his led-horse in the chase, now picked up his lines to follow behind the drag-riders. It had been the Woman's job, with help from Small, to hold the cows and steers after the men chased them back in twos and threes, puffing and blowing.

Having run off their spookiness, the cattle crossed Thunder Creek without another break.

The boys held the bunch on the far bench, and the tent was put up at the old camping place by the ford. The fire and the wagon would keep the cattle from trying to work back.

Leaving the Woman to cook supper, the Man changed saddles to the Lad's fresh led-horse and said explosively: "I'm riding back to talk to that fellow." He mounted and was gone in the October gloom.

As he topped the bank he could hear the bulldozer still muttering in the north-west. He covered the five miles at a smart trot and pushed his horse up the hill to the new grade.

Behind and before, the raw gash stretched straight as a ribbon, uphill and down.

"Set by compass, by gosh!" thought the Man. "The township line for sure. Must start at the survey stake on the riverbank—east. No good for a settler's road, though. O.K. for the winter, maybe. That's when they'll use it, I guess."

Only a four-wheeled drive could make those hills, and even it couldn't cross the swamps in summer. Once they'd run their test-holes they'd likely abandon it. One good spring run-off and there would be no more road!

He followed the cut along the sidehill, his rage growing. Coming across a man's range without a by-your-leave!

When he caught up with the monster he rode above and ahead and held up his hand. The brains of the beast looked out from the cat, which kept coming. The Man slithered his snorting horse to face it, and held up his hand again. The stoutly built young operator looked out again, shrugged his shoulders, and brought the bulldozer to a shuddering stop.

Dismounting, the rancher put a foot on the quivering step and spoke. The operator shrugged again and put a hand to his ear.

"Shut this damn thing off!" roared the Man.

The cat-skinner hesitated for a moment before complying. "Lookit," he said, "whoever you are, do you realize it costs like hell ever' time I stop this thing?"

"See if I care if it costs ten thousand bucks!" retorted the Man, his voice angry. "This is my lease, see? Another half mile and you'll be on my deeded land. That's my *property*, and you run this stink-wagon on to it, it'll cost you plenty! You pretty near lost me a bunch of cattle worth more than this damn thing!"

"Take 'er easy, old fellah." The skinner spoke with assumed jocularity. "You-all think you own the whole of this God-forsaken country because you have some li'l ole log shacks and a few wild cattle. We just got a lease, see?" He lit a cigarette and tossed the match away.

"Don't throw matches around this range, either!" The Man was red-faced, and wishing he wasn't. "Someday you'll burn up the country! Now listen." He made an effort at self-control. "Just what are you doing here, anyway?"

"Ain't you hayseeds never heard of oil?" The operator pretended surprise. "It's the latest thing. We find it, and you can say good-bye to that ole hay-burner of your'n!"—pointing to Monte. He went on with exaggerated patience, as if the grizzled rancher were a fractious child. "Now listen. *First* we build a road, see? *Then,* after freeze-up, when she's hard, a seismograph truck comes in. It'll leave mighty purty li'l red an' blue ribbons on the bushes, see? Then another outfit comes in and blows nice little holes so's to take out dinky samples. That's the way we find oil, see? Yep—that's right. So you know what I'm doing. I gets good pay and I goes where I'm told. And this is where I was told to go. I'm turning off south hereabouts to cross the crick—got it?" He pinched out his cigarette and lit another, but this time he broke the match and crushed it underfoot on the steel floor. "Have a *good* cigarette?" He held out his pack of Camels and shook one loose.

The Man detested American cigarettes and raised his hand to his shirt pocket for the makings. He was tired and angry, nettled by the patronizing tones and offer. But something told him—take a cigarette. You can't fight this fellow. He's under orders, and you'll have to go higher.

"O.K. Thanks." He took the proffered smoke. "Where's your boss?" he asked after a minute.

"Back at the stopping house. Our camp's there. He'll be sending a man for the night shift in a Jeep. I'll drive it back and sleep—I need it!" The operator rubbed his stubbly chin and his red-rimmed eyes.

They could hear the Jeep now, labouring up the soft dirt of the track.

"Well," said the Man, "if you're sure you are going to cross the creek here you'll soon be off my range. So I'll be getting back to the cattle. I'll have to ride down and have a talk with your boss, though. What's your name, by the way?"

"Larson—Rocky Larson," the operator replied, "and by the sound of it the boss is here!" The Jeep was rounding a corner not a hundred yards away. "He's a-driving. I know by the way he shifts them gears! My buddy don't clash 'em like that."

The lights came closer—stopped. Sure enough, there were two men. The one on the right jumped out and walked to the bulldozer, mounting the cat.

"What you stopped for, Larson?" shouted the driver. "You

haven't moved since we spotted your light a mile back! Don't you know—" He stopped abruptly.

Someone was tapping him on the shoulder and saying: "You the boss of this outfit?"

"I sure am!" was the quick retort. "And who in heck are you?"

"I'm the rancher who leases this land. Ranch is up round the corner six miles."

"You mean you live up here? We knew there was a homesteader around west some'eres. You him?"

The Man was nettled. He swallowed hard. "If you call an established ranch a homestead—yes. And if you'll study your map you'll find a few thousand acres under title in my name." He gave it. "And this is part of my lease. It runs from Thunder Creek to the Middle Fork, and it's all surveyed, at my expense. And I'd like to know why—"

"Mister," interrupted the foreman, "maybe you got this land leased for grazing. I don't dispute it. But *we* got it leased too, for oil. You know as well as me there ain't no private mineral rights hereabouts. Now we got rights as well as you. We ain't obliged to notify you unless we cross deeded land. We're turning south here to cross the creek, then up along the Elk-Run. So your ranch and your blessed ole cows won't be bothered yet awhile. Now, suppose you let me git out and put my man on the track he's to follow. I got to take the other back—he's done a twelve-hour shift. Er . . . pleased to meetcher . . ." He slid from the seat.

"I've done fourteen hours today, and I'm not through yet!" The Man was angry at the curt dismissal. "I nearly lost a bunch of cattle on account of that idiot. He should have shut off the engine when he saw the drive coming. That happens to be Law! I *have* lost one beast, and if he doesn't turn up—"

"Look," cut in the foreman, "maybe you fellows back here in the hills got time to B.S. We ain't. Time's money on this outfit. Any complaints or losses, you write in to the Makinac Gas and Oil at Edmonton. And don't ever think you can hold up an outfit like that by wasting our time. Holler when you're hurt —not before! And, say—listen. We don't shut down no cats for the Queen or the President, see? Now, we don't want no trouble—"

"Who pays for *my* wasted time?" the Man retorted hotly. But the foreman was talking to the night shift.

The Jeep started back, smoothly now. Evidently Rocky was at the wheel.

Cursing himself for a fool, the Man mounted and cantered back towards camp. The incident troubled him. He wished he had been more tactful, but if there was one thing that riled him it was rudeness. Property rights were a sort of religion with dedicated countrymen, but he supposed the industrial world thought of the wide-open spaces as their natural oyster and couldn't understand the views of a man who loved the land. All the trouble in the world, he thought, was based on lack of understanding, of communication. Why should a cat-skinner from Fort Worth or somewhere care about a few flowers on a hill-side?

Perhaps his attitude looked simply ludicrous to them, but the Man still thought he wouldn't sell flowers for greenbacks and would rather be poor and live in peace than be rich and have to put up with noise and stink. Didn't millionaires spend their industrial dollars to buy just what he already had!

This was worse than wolves!

It took three cups of coffee to calm him down.

Monte was rested now. The Man saddled and rode up the trail to relieve the Thunder Creek boys and let them eat and sleep till about four. The Lad had gone up ahead. There had to be at least two men with the cattle at night.

He found the herd, changed places with the rider on that side, and heard him go down to camp. The cattle had filled up and were bedded in a tight circle. There was no moon, and few stars showed. He couldn't find the Pointers in the north and had to guess the time. The cattle's breath made a fog-cloud over and around them.

The Man shivered in the raw cold. Riding well to one side he dismounted by a clump of willows and untied the extra sweater from behind his saddle-cantle. Slowly, quietly, making no movement which might spook the steers, he removed his canvas jacket, slipped on the woollen garment, and put on the jacket again. Wool inside and a windbreak outside was good for any amount of cold.

At the wagon he had already pulled on his heavy fur chaps. Now he drew his gloves from a pocket and worked his hands into them, then he pulled down his Stetson and mounted. He'd get no sleep tonight. The boys would be saddling up for a start about five o'clock. The Lad had got a few hours' sleep, so he'd be all right. The Man could hear him humming away to himself the other side of the cattle.

The Man heard a bawl from the creek and stiffened. If that was the yearling catching up it could be bad. Several steers were already on their feet, and the rest were uneasy.

He rode slowly, quietly, around to where the Lad, too, was listening. He caught his attention and spoke calmly. "See if you can sneak back south of the trail and get behind that critter. If it doesn't get here soon these steers'll go down the hill and we'll lose the bunch."

A horse whinnied just below. The Lad hesitated, then rode south to be off the trail. The yearling topped the bank and ran to the herd.

Something else was coming too. The Woman on Robin, his crooked white blaze just showing in the dim light. The pony whinnied again, softly. Monte answered. The Man rode forward.

"Well done," he said. "Well done, old girl. What happened?"

"Oh, I'd just got to sleep when I heard something across the creek. I thought it was a bear coming to raid the grub-wagon. The men are asleep somewhere south in the bush. So I put on my boots and looked out—and if it wasn't that yearling. I didn't dare breathe for fear I'd spook it and it 'ud turn back.

"What good luck the tent was off the trail far enough! Anyway, it started up the hill awfully slowly, so I thought I better push it along while it was in the mood in case it started bawling and brought the rest rushing down. I saddled Robin and followed it up. It did bawl once, and I hoped you heard it! I didn't dare call out to you, but Robin spoke to Monte, so I didn't need to anyway."

She brushed away two lacy snowflakes which had drifted down on her arm. "Br-r-r! It's cold."

"Well done," said the Man again. "Here, take my gloves, your hands are stone-cold."

"I have my own, thank you," she replied. "Forgot to put them on." She fumbled for them. "Must go to Small. I told her I'd only be a minute."

They reached the stopping house at mid-afternoon. By daylight those few flakes had turned to a snowstorm and the cattle walked steadily on, the north-west wind behind them, as they wound through the bushlands with snow-crusted backs. The riders dismounted from time to time and walked to warm their feet, trudging through the white mush, looking as uncomfortable as only cowboys on foot can look, the snow heavy on their shoulders, their hat-brims loaded, and their scarves tied over their ears.

Small, wet and cold, was told to ride in the wagon under a tarp, and chattered away to the Lad, who listened gravely.

The cattle were corralled, the tent put up, and while the Woman and Small were welcomed to the house the men threw themselves down in the tent with their outer clothes off and drifted into a much-needed sleep.

Someone was tapping at the tent-flap. The Man raised himself up on one arm. "Who's there?" he called.

A big, cheerful-looking individual peered in. He was dressed in clean khaki and was smoking a cigar. "I'm looking for the man who owns those cattle—you him?"

"That's me." The rancher was pulling on his boots. "What d'you want to see me about?"

"Oh, nothing much. You wanna come on out?" And as the Man emerged, pulling down his Stetson: "I'm the field superintendent of this outfit." He inclined his head towards the huddle of truck and trailers. "The foreman was telling me—say, have a cigar?"

"No thanks. Don't care for them." The rancher spoke stiffly.

"Oh well. . . . As I was saying, the foreman was telling me you had trouble on account of one of our bulldozers—that right?"

The Man sketched out the incident.

"Well now, that's too bad." The superintendent sounded sympathetic. "We don't reckon to upset anyone. It costs money to run those DH4s, and the skinners have orders to keep them walking. We didn't know there'd be cattle right there, and our men are mechanics, you know, not farmers.

"But I'll pass the word around to the boys to take it easy and stop when asked. I guess you surprised that boy—they aren't used to being jumped. Not that I blame you," he added hurriedly, seeing the spark in the other's eye.

"Now look," he went on, squatting on a box. "Why don't we just forget the whole thing? You haven't lost anything except a bit of time. So have we. You send in a bill and you'll be paid for any inconvenience. One of your men told me that your missing beast turned up.

"In the meantime, progress can't be stopped, you know. But live and let live is our motto, and we like to get along with people. We aim to benefit ever'body in the district. Why, look what we did for those Ayrabs in Saudi Arabia! Overnight they had things they never had before—a brand-new way of life!

"You stand to gain if we find oil. Why, mister, we make a good strike and first thing you'll have a gravel road. Maybe a town mighty close. Then you'll have the telephone, I shouldn't doubt, and a school, and your wife will be able to see the Hollywood pictures. And you'll not need to drive your cattle for miles—you'll be trucking them.

"See what I mean? And if we get a well on your place you'll be paid good rent. Just think a minute, mister, please. You'll have civilization up your way! You seem like an educated man, so I reckon you understand what I mean. And I know you can use money and facilities same as ever'body else!"

The rancher listened patiently, never taking his eyes from the oil-man's smiling, persuasive face. "Where do you live when you're home?" he asked, lighting the cigarette with which his fingers had been busy.

"Why, Minneapolis, I guess. Here, I'll give you my card. Any time you're down that way just drop around. If I'm not home my wife will make you folks welcome. We're all neighbours these days!"

The rancher puffed at his cigarette, blew on its glowing end, and spoke slowly. "Now, may I say something? I quite agree we might as well keep things peaceful if we can. But I'll tell you how I feel, just so there won't be any mistake.

"First of all, this progress you talk about maybe *can't* be stopped. But in the long view a day will come when oil won't have any more value—same as coal today. But people will still eat beef. So I reckon I'm just as progressive as you folks.

"Secondly, I didn't come up in here to help your kind of progress, because I don't give a damn for it. You'd feel the same if I tried to turn Minneapolis into a cattle range!

"Thirdly, I resent my land being messed about with and my cattle run without my say-so. And offering to pay afterwards doesn't appeal to me. Neither my time nor my property is for sale—forced sale.

"Fourthly, if you find oil, you gain, I lose. I lose my way of life. I simply don't want roads, schools, telephones, or picture-shows, and neither does my family. We came up here to get away from what they call 'civilization' today. There are different kinds, you know—and for my part I feel sorry for those Arabs. That's all. Except that I wouldn't trade my ranch for the whole city of Minneapolis. I've been there."

The oil-man stared. "Do you mean to tell me . . . ? Why, you must be joking! You mean, you'd rather ride a horse sixty miles than set comfortable in an auto . . . ?" He trailed off.

They both laughed. The tension was eased.

Later, talking it over with the Woman, the Man felt he must beware of committing himself. The superintendent had played the friendly hand well; but underneath that easy smile was a businessman, a tough, hard businessman.

As soon as possible after reaching town the Man called on his lawyer. That worthy listened with understanding and finally produced the statutes on land access and expropriation.

"According to this," he said, "you have only one right. That is the right to set certain terms under which you will permit peaceful access. Those terms permit you to demand payment in cash or kind for damage to stock, fences, and so on. If the company doesn't accept them they don't have to sign. Or if you don't like their counter-proposals you are equally free not to sign. Then it goes to Arbitration Court, and that—if I may use a strictly non-legal term—is a loaded shotgun with the company finger on the trigger. You'll probably lose on that, and they'll pay you less than any first offer.

"Bear in mind that the courts work as slowly as—hem—molasses in January. That the company will have a man whose full-time job is attending those courts, whereas you'll have to attend on your own time—it might be in the middle of haying or the roads may be bad. It would be a lot of grief, and you'll probably wish you hadn't started anything. I'm sorry, but that's the way it is."

"Now, I suggest," he went on after a pause, "I suggest that if they want to come on your deeded land—it's within their mineral lease—they will ask permission, but it's apt to be after they've got a start on you.

"Don't weaken. Stop them at the boundary if you can. Get the foreman to bring you in to me, and we'll draw up an agreement which will at least give you *some* protection. Better put a price on things before they do any damage. Keep it conservative and fair. I know you'll have no market price on some things, but the Law won't recognize that. If you remember a famous statement in fiction, *the Law is a h'ass.* It can't think.

"Whoever you talk to, ask for his credentials. Why, I've known a farmer sign an entry permission for an ordinary cat-skinner! He had no redress—didn't even know the fellow's name. So what the man had said meant nothing—and anyway he was sent on a job in another province.

"Certainly the oil people say they'll pay. Anyone can say that. But when it comes down to brass tacks, half the time they don't—adequately—and they always have the Law to uphold them technically. Please remember—this may shock your old-fashioned standards—government is much more interested in Makinac Oil than it is in you. Yes, it shocks me too.

"In our—hem—democracy today, it's unpopular to fight progress. It's not the custom—and custom, my dear fellow, is the basis of Law."

The lawyer made a little tent—or was it a chapel?—of his stubby fingers, and bowed slightly, as to some unseen force, and resumed.

"History repeats itself. Property rights were once thought to be sacred. Our children—or yours, I haven't any—are taught in school that the old Norman kings were bad, because they turfed out some peasants to make a hunting forest. But the same children are taught all about the—er—blessings of progress with an American 'ō,' in spite of the fact that the industrial world practises the same skulduggery. Progress means change. A rather peevish god, I fear, but still a god.

"So, much as you and I may dislike this thing, if you fight against this—hem—'True God,' you—we—are considered bad men."

He glanced at the clock, one he had begged from the school board when they electrified the classroom timepieces, and then rose. "Sorry for the lecture," he said blandly, as he extended his hand. "There's no fee."

The Man left, feeling that his free days were numbered. He liked the lawyer. He savoured his Dickensian manner, his shabby Dickensian "chambers" with books piled higgledy-piggledy.

He now realized the full impact of the words *Minerals in the Crown,* which were rather casually stamped on his land deeds.

It was time to take the womenfolk to the airport. The bags they had brought on the wagon were repacked, and they all got in the taxi. . . .

Small was going to a boarding school at the coast. She did look pretty small as she stepped up the ramp with her mother.

Chapter 29

Never had the sun shone more benignly. Never had the birds sung more joyously. The piping of white-throated sparrows, the wild, sweet notes of thrushes, even the hoarse, repeated notes of the phoebes beneath the eaves, all spoke for the season.

The Woman was hanging multi-coloured towels on her wash-line and the Man, riding in from his work, checked his horse to enjoy the picture she made as she reached high with clothes-pegs.

No wolves had bothered the cattle for months, and his almost four hundred acres of hay were beginning to come into blossom, the purple heads of brome bending in the soft wind, the bees droning in the blue alfalfa blooms.

All was quiet except for the *frou-frou* of the hay rippling in the wind, the chanting of the birds, and the dusty thumps of a horse rolling in the corral.

He caught the Woman's eye, and she waved and blew him a kiss.

All this, he thought, and Small too. (She was home for the holidays.) All this they had made with their hands. They had worked, they had scrimped to achieve this. It was not just a place—a business—a house. It was home.

They owed no man. All the land was paid for.

But even as a wave of thankfulness flowed over him, something still nagged at the back of his mind. Something like foreboding. He was sitting under his own fig-tree, but for how long? In his heart of hearts he knew a worm was gnawing at the root. Who has said: "Thou shalt sow but not reap"? The crop they wanted was a dignified old age in the spot of their choice. But perhaps the happiness was in doing, rather than having . . .

"Too nice a day to think of such things," the Man decided, and led Monte through the spruce, as squirrels chattered and made impudent remarks to the horse.

Behind the peaceful scene the props were being changed even more rapidly than he had foreseen. A road to the west, several miles across the creek to be sure, had already brought settlers, many of whom would go broke, leaving the land scarred behind them.

His own ranch boundaries were secure against them but not against the Expropriation Act, which allowed the government to take land for almost any fool reason.

The tourist trade was being drummed up, now that a railway was coming from the interior, as well as a road through the mountains.

Only last fall hunters had found their way by Jeep, following the frozen seismograph road, and had shot one of his best crossbred steers. "Didn't know what it was—looked like the devil in chaps," they'd said when the Man rode up. They had paid for the steer—but it had been a forced sale.

Now a company had struck oil only seven miles east, on Yellow Creek . . .

And only a month ago the Man had met a bulldozer intent on crossing the north end of the valley. He had stopped the operators, got hold of the foreman, and gone into town. The lawyer had drawn up an agreement for possible damages, stressing damage to land by way of erosion. But in the meantime the catskinner had been put on another route, straight north, so as to "take the heat off" for the time being.

As the Man left town he had been amazed at the development (that hated word!) that had crept up on the little settlement. Two big hotels now, both with cocktail bars, softly lit . . . Cocktails! And a third going up. The Hudson's Bay store had been remodelled as a serve-yourself. The streets were being paved and lit by electricity. There was a super-market by the church, which almost hid that pioneer edifice.

Noise—the screeching noises of commerce and industry—was everywhere. A new brick post office was being built, impersonal, institutional. Getting your mail would never be the same.

And the people. In masses. Mostly strange faces. Top oil-men carrying glossy brief-cases. Field superintendents in olive drab. Roughnecks enjoying a week off. The restaurants crowded. Jukeboxes blaring. Drunks. Oil-wives buying ten cents' worth of candy for their offspring while an old-timer waited patiently to get a two-hundred-dollar grocery order filled.

Oil talk. Technological talk. "The Jurassic" . . . "stratas" . . . that constantly repeated "that's righ'" in the accents of Texas. It was like a foreign country! Merchants greeted him not with, "How's the cattle?" but, "How's the oil up your way?"

No more wagons rolling. No more riders sitting their horses easily, as if they belonged. The livery barn had been pulled down, and a shiny garage had taken its place. Three more were going up, and the stream of cars the Man dodged as he crossed the street had licence plates from Kansas, from Oklahoma, from Texas and Minnesota. A gaudily pennanted car came down the street, the loud-speaker blaring something about bingo.

As the Man strode out to the farm a mile away, where he now had to leave his horses, he thought of the ugliness and the vulgarity of this seething, frantic child of the technological revolution, and told himself that now he was a stranger, an alien, where he had been a citizen, a Canadian.

Chapter 30

Next morning found the Woman taking in the wash, and the Man halter-breaking a colt, while Small divided her time and attention between them. As she carried one side of the clothes-basket she suddenly said: "May we have a little ride this afternoon? I'm just longing to get on old Robin—and let's see if the raspberries are ripe on Wild Horse Point? But I don't want to go alone—there might be a bear!"

"Run and see what your father says," was the reply. "Then he can keep the bears away. I don't like them either, and if we take a lunch we don't want them coming along with their paper-bags, do we? For the crumbs, you know."

Off to the corral skipped Small, reciting in her high little voice: "The common cormorant or shag. . . ." She wondered what a shag was.

The colt was awfully wild, and Small sat on the corral fence watching it lunge and plunge while her Daddy talked steadily and calmly to it. "Come on, old-timer, you'll only hurt yourself. And if you don't wise up, why maybe I'll have to try a trip-hobble, and you aren't going to like that!"

The colt plunged again, and the Man gave the rope an extra turn over the snubbing-post. As the colt reached the end of the slack he reared and fell. The Man loosened the rope. "Come on, get up!" The colt rose gingerly. The red, flaring nostrils relaxed. The wild eyes softened. The Man walked carefully up the rope, and keeping to one side of the animal's shoulder, watching its forefeet, slowly raised his hand.

The eyes showed terror again, but the Man's voice droned on. "Sho' now, little feller, loosen up a bit."

The colt's ears flicked forward, his full attention given to the voice. The Man's hand reached to touch its poll and scratched softly under the rope halter, easing the tension, smoothing out the ruffled mane. The colt raised its muzzle, blew softly in the Man's face. "That's more like it," he said softly, and was aware of a small voice saying:

"He's good now, Daddy. You aren't going to call him 'Old-timer,' are you? I think 'Rex' would be a much nicer name."

"Oh." The Man smiled. "I call him anything when I'm just talking! Like I call you 'tiddlywinks' or 'chick' sometimes." He dropped the rope and began to roll a smoke. "Does your mother want something?" he ventured, as he licked the paper and gave it a twist.

Small told him the plan.

"O.K., chick! We'll go right after dinner, so hurry and help your mother, eh?"

The three rode north, chatting happily. The Man needed just such relaxation to, as he said, "recharge his batteries." Robin, getting a bit stiff now, didn't like Small's insistence on a short canter, and she had to dig him pretty hard with her heels.

The Man, noticing, said: "I'll have the colt broke gentle for you by next year, and you can name him to suit yourself."

"I've already done that." Small smiled. "Remember? It's Rex."

On either side of the cow-path raspberry clumps showed the red of ripe fruit, but Small insisted on going to the point. "These ones are too dusty," she explained. And when they got to the point, on the lower side of the little bushy flat, they were all glad they hadn't wasted time. The raspberry bushes here were simply loaded and the berries were clean and bright, for no cattle had been making paths through them.

The bears were there all right, though Small could see only two black faces with pricked ears and small eyes, and presently, as they stood up to survey the intruders, two sets of black arms and rather clawy feet hanging before them.

The Man said: "Get out of here!" and the bears got, galloping off like a couple of woolly dogs.

They all set to picking. The sun was hot, the birds were silent except for the cheeping of some fledgling warblers which were plundering the fruit, and the sharp, cranky notes of a pair of kingbirds. The berries went *plop-plop* into the lard pails tied at the pickers' waists. The Man kept one eye on the little, tawny head he could barely see above the rustling canes. The horses out on the grass stood in a little group, heads together, tossing them against the flies.

Then they heard the bulldozers. They were coming down from Moose Ridge, one behind the other.

The little group, their pails almost full, gathered together and watched, as the cats threw trees, brush, and dirt to one side, the trees collapsing to either side slowly, silently, and inevitably, the dirt rolling sideways under the heavy blades, sending up a choking dust.

"Of all the nerve!" the Man burst out. "I told that foreman only last month not to come straight down that hillside. There'll be an awful gully come spring! I'd best ride over, confound it." He mounted and galloped off.

The Woman saw the bulldozers stop, saw the Man gesticulating and pointing. She knew he was angry.

"Didn't I tell you fellows not to cut down this hill?" the Man was saying. "There's plenty of other routes you could take, and if you'd let me know—as was agreed—I'd have shown you."

"I weren't there," the skinner retorted. "Boss is back a-ways. Talk to him."

The Man rode on to the Jeep which was just coming in view.

The foreman said: "Look. You signed a paper, didn't you? Maybe it said something about hills, but we got to go the way we want. We got right of access from you—we had it anyways—but we don't go for orders, see? We aim to treat ever'body alike, an' no-one else ever bothered about a li'l ole sidehill. Ain't no grass there anyways."

"That's not the point," the Man replied, and then said no

more. What was the use of trying to tell people that a cut such as they had started would erode into a gully which could eventually cross his hay-flat to the creek, widening year by year?

The foreman was saying: "If we've done any damage, we'll pay. Ain't more'n a couple acres involved anyways."

"Couple of acres!" the Man half shouted. "Why, man, my whole hay-flat is involved. Anyway, the damage is done now and I'll see my lawyer. On your way! Oh, and when you get to the fence you'll have to make a proper gate or I'll have cattle in my crop-land."

"Just a minute before you go," said the foreman. "Take it easy. We ain't got no fencing crews to come sixty miles to make a gate or two gates! We pay fifty dollars a gate. That's forty dollars more'n it'll cost you to make one. The wire is here and you got posts and tools. All the farmers do it, and it's the easiest money they ever made, and they know it. Or you can hire someone if you want, and you still win."

"My agreement with the company says they are responsible for damage, so you'll have to fix the gates like I said," the Man retorted sharply.

"What makes you so cantankerous anyways?" The foreman sounded puzzled. "Why should you be too proud to take good money same as ever'body else? The company's spending money like a blessed emperor, and the farmers a-holding out their hands for it!"

"Because I'm not working for Makinac Oil & Gas—that's why. Any time I want a job with them I'll go ask for it. I don't work as a forced labourer for any man. In other words I'm not for sale. Get it?" The air of finality in the Man's tones reached the foreman's mind.

"O.K." he said. "Have it your own way. But we got no tools ner men right now. So if your cattle do get in we can't help it. Course, we pay fer any damage they do. Maybe that's what you want, eh?"

The Man did not reply, but turned his horse around, thinking: "Pay, pay, pay!" Was this a sheriff's sale?

The bulldozers rolled on. The seismograph trucks were pressing close on their heels, and the testing crew wanted to be across the creek by evening. As they rolled on they filled the ford with logs—big green trees, which were attacked with gusto, their roots charged at, and then pushed over with heightened blades. *His* trees! He saw them fall with a crash, saw them pushed into the water, splashing the bushes with mud. His trees! They'd balk at paying for "a few li'l ole poplar trees." No Arbitration Court would allow more than ten cents each. Trees weren't half so important as motor-cars.

Oh damn!

As the man rejoined the berry-pickers the bulldozers, safe across the creek, swung around the point. The little party, mounted, had to move out of their way. They watched the belching giants roar right through the raspberry patch which had given them fruit for so many years, throwing the dirt to right and left, tossing the canes on high—pitiful vines clinging, revolving with the inexorable Caterpillar tracks—soiled, bleeding fruit staining their shining steel.

Small burst into tears.

The Man cursed, raised a clenched hand; he dropped it, realizing the inadequacy of the futile gesture.

Now they were unsaddling in the corral, the Man still red-faced. He was feeling his years. This was not the wilderness he was fighting; this was cunning, scheming, money-mad man.

The Woman said gently: "I know it's too grisly for words; but don't give those creatures the satisfaction of your dying of an apoplectic fit, for goodness' sake!"

Small's back was to them, her chestnut head against Robin's flank as she tugged at the cinch.

She was half crying still, and muttering, and something she said sounded uncommonly like: "Sonsa bitches!" which startled the Woman, who looked at the Man.

He was grinning, half-shamefacedly, half-pleased, at that expression of loyalty from his daughter.

Chapter 31

The rancher won that round, in a way. The agreement the lawyer had drawn up read: ". . . make good any damage to the satisfaction of the owner of the deeded land."

Money apparently was not satisfactory; as the company found out. They sent out a fencing crew and put in two gates. They also sent a cat to alter the lay of the road, and plugged the one down Moose Ridge to prevent a spring wash-out. And when they abandoned it, they filled it in and seeded it to crested wheat grass, as well as hauling out the big trees from the ford so that the cattle could use it again.

The Man hated the mess they'd made, hated the raw, unsightly gashes through the bush. He picked up and burned the garish plastic ribbons they had left alongside their oil-road.

He had only one cause for satisfaction. Apparently no large quantity of oil underlay Deep Springs Ranch. The next season the company abandoned the whole area, at least temporarily.

But not before several good cows had died under suspicious circumstances in early spring. The Man had seen them on their knees, licking the mud at the test-holes. He drove them away. But next day they were dead, swollen and horrible. It looked like lead poisoning. He could not send for the veterinary for over

a week, as the creeks were high. When at last that expert came the carcasses had deteriorated so badly that a positive identification of cause was not possible. The Man went to Calgary to see the company, which swore they had not—never did—use red lead in their test-holes, although the Man had been told by a friend in Calgary who worked for a similar company that this practice was quite common.

This conversation was followed by a long and bitter correspondence, to no avail. The company quoted an "expert opinion" to the effect that the cattle had died from want of mineral supplement; to which the rancher submitted the fact that only cattle along that particular trail had been affected. All the rest on the south range showed no such symptoms.

His lawyer said during a consultation that, had the company struck oil on the ranch, they would probably have paid market-price without a word of dispute. They were forced, under the terms of their lease, to do so much exploration anyway. And they evidently had not expected much in the way of results on the ranch—hence their cavalier attitude.

"You'll remember those cattle Bidwell lost on the Doig? About eight head? Well, this same company went no further than sending a man to look at them. And they gave him a cheque for over a thousand dollars! But they had found oil there—and public relations were important.

"I expect they addressed Bidwell as 'Sir,' to boot."

Chapter 32

Six months later the Man and the Woman held a conference. He hadn't felt so well lately. The doctors had told him to watch his heart, not to work so hard, and to avoid being upset.

"Perhaps we should try to sell out?" hazarded the Woman.

"Not for that," he replied. "I'd as soon die here as anywhere. No. Other things being equal, we'd never leave. But with the rate of change pressing on us, should we stay? Would we be happy?

"I mean," he added, "I can feel in my bones that what we have seen so far is just the beginning."

He walked over to the window and stood gazing silently across the meadows, all backed by neat clumps of woodland. This was the land to which his heart and hands had been bound for so long, but under the inexorable laws of expansion it would —it must—change. Perhaps they should leave—for good. Leave while the sweet savour was in their mouths, a savour they could carry with them—where?

If they did go, they should never return. It would only hurt. He would see hunters—sportsmen!—blundering through the woodland aisles in outlandish red caps, armed with compasses and knives and telescope-sighted guns, to shoot the animals he loved. Not for their meat and hides, not to sustain life, but to obey an urge, a compulsion, which—although twisted and warped—was yet kin to his own compulsion to pioneer.

Only they would not accord that respect to the wilderness which somehow prompts the true countryman to step softly and to avoid loud conversation, the leaving of untidy camps, the trampling of wildflowers, and all those acts which mark the intruder who does not understand the quietude and awesomeness of unspoilt creation.

Such men were like Priestley's tourists, who swarmed over the United States to break the monotony, where their fathers had come to break the land.

For him to see all this—he who had been told not to let himself be upset—might well be death in its most literal form.

He could see a survey mound from where he stood, a survey mound within which was a copper stake for which he had paid fifteen dollars; and yet it was not his, for cut into it was the seal of British Columbia and the warning: "One hundred dollars' fine for removal of this stake."

He, under the Law of the Province, had been obliged to have the ranch surveyed at his expense, not as a whole, but subdivided into sections and quarters. He had, as secretary of the Cattlemen's Association, protested to the minister of Lands that since government, representing the people, was the ultimate beneficiary of survey, it should assume the cost, as was accepted elsewhere. But the protests of the Association were of no avail.

In an unchanging world this might be all very well; but he saw now that government would not permit a *status quo,* that it had long-term plans for what it called "multi-use." The Expropriation Act would allow it to take so much for roads when the time was ripe; so much for industry; so much for parks and recreation, for dams, for towns, if need be.

And all who came after him would benefit from the surveys which had cost him so dear, without a thought for the man who had known no better than to bury himself in a wilderness. He could see acres which he had made productive, land he had seized from the wild, land which before his coming had yielded neither sustenance to man nor taxes to government, made the site of a town or a crude-oil establishment. He could see rows of jerry-built houses and trampled untidy yards where once he had harvested the sweet hay; derelict cars scattered about, as he saw elsewhere. Where once had been a home, he saw offices with filing cabinets and clattering typewriters. Bulldozers might well demolish his spruce-grove, with its crossbills and its merry squirrels, boorish hands might dump loads of gravel on his flowery lawn, and a cocktail lounge would perhaps occupy the place of his neat corrals and haystacks. People would sit and sip their drinks and gaze at TV, while the Greatest Show on Earth—lit by the northern lights, set to the music of running water and the cries of night-birds—would go unheeded by those who would never know—or care—that once a Man, a Woman, and a child lived here in thankfulness and sufficiency.

Those who would come would have their problems too. And the problems would be worse ones, for most of the people would be slaves to commerce, having come not to enjoy the country but to make enough money to leave and return to . . . Minneapolis? . . . Dallas . . . Vancouver? . . .

They would complain of isolation, the long winters, the cost of living . . .

And some would die before they "made their pile" . . .

And some might live to see, like him, colossal changes. A new era in which oil and gas had no part, so that they found themselves jobless, with the squirrels and the rats scampering through the empty offices. An era when some synthetic factory-product would replace timber products, as the horse had replaced the ox, and the gasoline engine the horse; as atomic power already marked petroleum for obsolescence.

But, he thought, they would still need meat and grain. Eventually, over a long term, agriculture and stock-raising would still be the basic industries for man. Yet he remembered that his lawyer had said: "This may shock you, but government is more interested in Makinac Oil than in you."

Yes, it might be better to sell now. They had been allowed to know this valley, to love it, to sustain themselves from its bounty. He knew it had never really been his; for, as the Crees say, man's possessions are few and the earth is the Manitou's.

Even though today's landlord, the State, is no better than the Norman lords of old, yet God is not mocked. Therefore he had to accept the changes. There is a purpose in life for those who seek, and now he had to seek, and seeking find. After he had got used to the idea of leaving, a way would be made clear.

The Woman sat jotting down the pros and cons of staying or leaving.

On the one hand, this was the home they loved, the country they loved, and the work they loved.

On the other, the Boy was satisfied with Australia; the Kid had a job down at the coast in a bank; Small, a teen-ager now, wouldn't be home much, and later on, if she married . . .

Help was increasingly hard to get. All the young fellows were working for oil companies or survey crews.

The Lad now had a small bunch of cattle of his own and a saddle-horse the Man had given him as a colt, and was anxious to start up for himself. Only last week he had staked a little valley up on the Elk-Run. He had been a real godsend, but they knew they would not be able to keep him much longer now.

Finally, although their lease still stood, no-one could foretell the future—in spite of the present departure of the oil-men. Government was talking about a main road east and west, so that tourists and hunters would be able to get to the mountains; and this road, if built as proposed, would cut right through his ranch.

"Imagine a stream of cars hooting by, not a quarter of a mile from the house, making everything dusty!" exclaimed the Woman when she heard about it. "And probably filling stations and hot-dog stands. And people with swarms of kids picking our berries and coming to the springs for water. And hunters shooting our ruffed grouse. And . . ."

She trailed her words off and sat looking out across the valley.

"Well, old girl," the Man said, "there are plenty of people who wouldn't mind a bit, if you can believe me. I'd hate it as much as you—worse, actually, because I'm older and crustier. But, if we did decide to sell, all this would actually make it easier—because most people want to drive a car, or a station-wagon, to the door."

The odds were heavily on a sale, but they left it at that for the time being.

That fall the Man went to Calgary to attend a stock sale. There he ran into a fellow he knew, who told him he'd been talking to a sheep-and-cattle man in Miles City looking for a ranch up in Canada. He promised to write to the Montana man.

Chapter 33

It was March. The valley lay almost free from snow, but the early chinook had blown itself out. Sitting at dinner, the Man and the Woman heard the plane, and from the window saw it land on the meadow. Two men and a woman alighted and came towards the house.

It was the man from Miles City and his wife, with their pilot.

The Woman cooked more moose-steaks and made another pot of coffee. Then the pilot rose from the table. He said to the Montanan: "I'd best be getting back to Edmonton. When do you want me to pick you up?"

The American said: "Tomorrow, I guess. That is"—turning to the rancher—"if you're in a selling mood and can keep us overnight for a look-around?"

The Man replied: "Better make it three days from now—if you don't mind moose-meat. I've got a lot of country to show you, and we'll have to ride. We've plenty of room, and I don't want to sell a pig-in-a-poke!"

The pilot nodded, left, and they heard the plane take off.

The couple was more than pleased with the ranch. They had been shown every trail, every spring. They had seen the big, high stacks of hay and oat-bundles. The four-foot sheaves impressed them. "Lucky to get a foot and a half down in dry old Montana!" they said.

They looked over the equipment, the brood-mares, the cattle. "Real good cattle!" they exclaimed.

Best of all, they thought the miles of high upland range would be good for sheep under herd. The Montanan had about three thousand woollies "down home," but the lease fees and taxes were eating up the profits, and the range was dwindling, which was why he wanted to move north.

The Man set a price for the whole outfit as a running concern.

The price was agreeable, the terms agreed to. Only, could the Man continue to run the place till April, since it would take that long to arrange for shipping the sheep and some other equipment they wanted? The Man agreed, and it was decided they'd all meet in two weeks' time to sign the papers, as the new buyers had to get back right away.

The money would keep them in reasonable comfort for the rest of their lives, the Man and the Woman decided. They would find some peaceful spot in the older settlements, some place where industry had browsed around, and finding little, had headed for the new bonanza along the Peace.

The new folks were real stock people—that was a comfort. Young too. More adaptable. Themselves products of the machine age, and not quite—the man, at all events—the easy-going type. He was . . . harder. More business-like. He'd do all right.

Two weeks later the ranch changed hands for good. The lawyer came to the door of his sanctum when all was over and the four were passing through the outer office. The premises were larger now. The lawyer had a junior partner. Two blonde-headed secretaries sat at their typewriters.

"Stand up, girls!" said the man of Law. "Stand up and say good-bye to the last of the free men!"

Epilogue

The Man and the Woman looked at each other in the south-bound bus. Both had been occupied with their own thoughts.

Hers had been of the grey cat they had to leave behind with the faithful old stove, the home-made furniture, the Dutch dresser.

The books and other intimate things had been crated. They would be sent on when there was an address. An address? Never before in her life had she been without such a thing! She tried not to think of the mountains, of the garden, of the horses and chickens, for she knew she would cry.

His thoughts revolved about the cattle, the hay-meadow, the corrals and fences. The things he had spent his blood and guts on.

He thought of those weary, endless days out on the new breaking, picking roots like a day-labourer of old, yet feeling rich—and happy. He thought of that first time he had seen Deep Springs, that sense of the explorer reaching his goal which this had given him. Venturing into the unknown is like salt to the pioneer type, he pondered; and then, quite suddenly, he thought, "This is just another adventure! Life is never over when you can make a new beginning!"

Perhaps he could take up his painting, and better still, his writing. He had always wanted to write and illustrate a book about birds, and now he could gather and edit his notes . . .

And then for some reason he thought of that last wolf; it had been forced to make a new beginning way back there . . .

As if she had read his thoughts, the Woman said: "I feel rather like that wolf. We pushed him out, and now *we* are pushed out by Mr. Makinac! But never mind, we'll find a cosy place, and you can write about it all."

"So I will, by Jove!" he replied. "We'll think of the happy years, and be glad."

The Woman answered softly: "The happiest years of my life. But we'll find lots more together—shan't we?"

"Of course we shall!" the Man agreed.